3.10.'80

JANET SARTIN ON BEAUTIFUL SKIN

JANET SARTIN ON BEAUTIFUL SKIN

BY

JANET SARTIN

with

JULIE DAVIS

DOUBLEDAY & COMPANY, INC.
GARDEN CITY, NEW YORK
1980

Library of Congress Cataloging in Publication Data

Sartin, Janet.
Janet Sartin on Beautiful Skin.

Includes index.
1. Skin—Care and hygiene. I.
Davis, Julie, 1956– joint author.
II. Title.
RL87.S27   646.7′26
ISBN: 0-385-14227-7
Library of Congress Catalog Card Number 78–68368

BOOK DESIGN BY BENTE HAMANN

Contents

1. SKIN DEEP: THE JANET SARTIN PHILOSOPHY — 1

2. WHICH SKIN TYPE ARE YOU? — 9

3. THE WORLD'S BEST (AND SIMPLEST) SKIN CARE SYSTEM — 26

4. MAKING MAKEUP WORK FOR YOU — 46

5. PROBLEM SKIN: BREAKTHROUGH OR BREAKOUT — 79

6. YOUR FUTURE FACE — 108

7. APPROACHING THE VINTAGE YEARS — 115

8. BODY ESSENTIALS — 123

9. SKIN NUTRITION — 138

10. TAKE CARE — 142

11. COSMETIC SURGERY: PROMISCUOUS OR PRESCRIBED? — 153

12. MY MOST FREQUENTLY ASKED (AND ANSWERED) QUESTIONS — 159

13. CELEBRITY COMPLEXIONS — 166

14. THE SARTIN TOUCH: THE SALON TREATMENT — 178

INDEX — 185

This book is dedicated
to the memory of my beloved mother
and my late husband,
their devotion and love made all things possible,
and to my son, Cary,
who is devoting his extraordinary talents
to bringing the Janet Sartin experience
to my readers.
And to my charming and attractive clientele,
many of whom have traveled
from all over the world
to be benefited and made happy
by my beauty products.

I wish to acknowledge with thanks the encouragement shown by Louise Gault, my editor, and Alex Gotfryd, my art director; Connie Clausen, my literary agent whose support brought this project to fruition; and Julie Davis, whose understanding and perception were most helpful in the writing of this book.

JANET SARTIN ON BEAUTIFUL SKIN

1.

Skin Deep: The Janet Sartin Philosophy

Beautiful, radiant skin is not just a matter of vanity. Today's active way of life demands perfection in the way you look. Your skin needs the same meticulous, fastidious care you give your hair, your clothes, your home. Neglecting your skin is a bad habit and I'd like to show you how easy it is to stop it.

Good looks start with immaculate skin; there's no getting away from it. Not even the most deft makeup artistry can hide or compensate for lifeless skin or skin that is plagued by acne; beautiful skin should never be masked by makeups that cover over. These two premises I learned from the start.

I first became interested in the art and science of skin care when, in 1937, I began working with Erno Laszlo, the European expert who opened a whole new world of beauty to a select group of women. My total dedication came in 1946 when I started my own business and my own research, developing skin care products that did what they were supposed to do, quite unlike those that had fancier labels which promised results they could not possibly guarantee.

I know that my preparations accomplish *two* jobs, not just one. My cleansing preparations correct the imbalance of your skin while they cleanse. My makeup preparations continue this correction while they beautify your skin. I will be telling you about all my products throughout my book, what you should expect from them and what ingredients you should look for in other products if you cannot get mine.

I can't speak for the various manufacturers on the market, but I will try to indicate the mediums that are right for you and your skin.

My work has led me to be called a prophet by many beauty critics—the High Priestess of Skin. It was precisely because I did, and still do, feel that I have an inherent ability to see skin in a special light that I chose to make the beautification of skin my life's work. I will be the first to admit though that I am a bit unorthodox in my beliefs, at least by the prevailing standards of beauty.

I believe, for instance, that you should never cover up your skin's shortcomings; that will certainly not make them go away. You must help your skin attain a perfect balance which will help prevent the problems from recurring.

I believe that your skin does not need a coat of foundation or base—what outdated words!—before you can be seen by the outside world. After all, you want to enhance your complexion, not build a house.

And I'll tell you something else right now, something I'm sure many of you won't want to hear: your once-a-month facial at the twenty-clients-an-hour operation nearest you isn't doing your skin a bit of good either!

If I'm speaking frankly, it is because I want you to know that *I am just as adamant about not doing the wrong things for your skin as I am about doing the right ones.*

I ask the same serious commitment to beautiful skin from clients who see me at my salon and now from you. There are no crash courses to a glowing complexion and I don't want you to be misled by anyone who says there are. I have been perfecting my system through firsthand experience for more than thirty years of personally caring for, correcting, and creating the most beautiful, youthful faces in the world.

My system has been refined, made sophisticated and simplified, with a minimum of preparations and an easy way of using them. Having dozens of different jars in all shapes and colors might look impressive at first, but you would soon realize that they add up to just a lot of clutter.

I won't lie to you—achieving and maintaining good-looking skin requires constant care, but there is no need for a complicated routine that you probably wouldn't even try to follow. My system is one that every woman and every man can follow for the rest of their life. You won't have to worry about being tempted by any charlatan's bag of tricks anymore, and that's a promise I can keep.

Starting to care about your skin at an early age is important because it is easier to maintain a youthful appearance than it is to recapture one. But it is never "too late." Through my many years in this field, I have learned that no skin problem is ever hopeless: no matter what it is, no matter how severe, your skin can always fight back and win. Don't be afraid of being honest. Please don't hide behind your makeup or your sunglasses and certainly not in a dark corner, as we have all felt we'd like to do at one time or another. Skin responds fantastically to proper care and attention, at every age. And I can help you bring your skin to its fullest potential.

All my principles are long-standing and based on fact. I won't try to sell you short with a newly hatched scheme or newly invented theory. We have had quite enough myths popularized in the past few years, all at your skin's expense. Misconceptions, foisted on the public by the beauty and makeup world, have left women more confused than ever about where to turn for help. You have been told that everything from chicken embryos to placentas to queen bee honey to rubbing on vitamin E capsules can work miracles on your skin. What nonsense!

The newest wrinkle—or, as its manufacturers would like you to think, wrinkle-deterrent—is the moisturizer. Well, nothing could be worse for an oily skin than a coating of more oil; your face will become sluggish. And though dry skin needs to be nourished, it should not be laden with a greasy substance. I'm a realist dealing in facts. Fads leave me cold!

Fact One The most important benefits from skin care can be achieved through a constructive program, one that has accumulative, long-range results. I spell care with three c's: cleansing, correction, and consistency, three words that will become an integral part of your beauty vocabulary.

A CONSTRUCTIVE PROGRAM = CLEANSING + CORRECTION + CONSISTENCY

Proper cleansing is paramount. Without it, skin loses its vitality and glow. Many women who have dry skin are afraid of washing; they fear this will further dry their skin. Improper cleansing and a lack of attention will indeed do more harm, but the correct care will benefit all skins—dry and oily alike—immensely. I'll tell you how in a chapter later on, but you should know now that there will be individual guidelines for every skin type. I believe in a soap-and-water routine for your face but the soap must be formulated for your own skin because:

Fact Two Every skin has its own personality and your skin care regime must reflect that.

The second objective of my program is correction for dry, oily, sensitive, and allergic skins. The proper cleansing preparations correct as they cleanse. Dry skin is enriched; oily skin is normalized; sensitive and allergic skins are soothed.

CLEANSING AND CORRECTION WORK HAND IN HAND

You must be as consistent in your approach to skin care as you are with everything else you undertake. Let's face it: it's tempting to be careless. Haven't we all felt too tired, one night, to do what we were supposed to, too tired to brush our teeth or to remove our makeup? It's easy to say to yourself, "I'll do it in the morning" or "I'll catch up tomorrow." But there's one thing wrong with this attitude: it doesn't work. By tomorrow, you'll have fallen behind and won't be able to catch up. And more often than not, by tomorrow you will have forgotten what you were supposed to do.

If you're lazy about caring for your skin, you won't acheive the complex-ion you want. But if you adhere to your routine each day, every day will bring you better and better results, which is what we're all striving for.

Tell yourself that you will follow my program faithfully. Neither you nor I will tolerate anything less.

CONSISTENCY IS ESSENTIAL FOR IMPROVING THE QUALITY OF YOUR SKIN

Fact Three You can accomplish your goal through your own efforts. Depending on your particular skin, your program will consist of a two or three times a day routine; but you mustn't be scared off by this. Following this routine will soon be second nature to you and you will feel more than rewarded when you see your skin glowing and vibrant. When you receive your first compliment, you'll know you've accomplished what you set out to do.

Caring for yourself shouldn't be looked at as drudgery, certainly not when it can make you more beautiful.

Fact Four Skin is a great tattle-taler. It can give away bad eating habits. It can make you look older or younger, depending on whether or not you give it the tender loving care it deserves. I spell care with two p's as well as three c's; they stand for *protection* and *prevention*. You must always be on guard to protect your skin from factors that can harm it, such as the weather, tension, and anxiety. You must always try to prevent problems— you will see that this is far easier to do than solving them once they've become full-blown.

Are you thinking that your skin needs more drastic measures for improvement? If you do, I have a feeling we might disagree. A steady, thorough program will accomplish more than you think. You won't achieve the results you're looking for by resorting to harsh procedures such as recommended "home remedies" like sloughing preparations and abrasive scrub pads. They won't renew your skin nor make it look and perform as it did years ago. Contrary to what you desire, this stripping destroys your skin's natural vitality by exposing new skin to the elements (sun, wind, cold) before it can shield itself. Don't treat your face as though it were a kitchen floor with a waxy buildup—the image isn't pretty, the treatment isn't pretty and, worst of all, the results aren't pretty. Rather, you must work with your skin's natural properties—its elasticity, its gradual cellular renewal ability, its eager responsiveness.

Think of your skin as a luscious organ. Spend as much time nurturing your skin as you do your plants and you'll have beautiful skin that will stay beautiful forever.

Remember that your skin is fragile. Think about adopting a new attitude toward your face. When you touch your skin, be gentle, never rough or quick. Think of making your skin comfortable and you, happy. Clear your mind of all other thoughts when you are caring for your face. Skin is more receptive when you are feeling tranquil and at ease. This is the approach I take and it works.

I want to establish a rapport with you right now. Throughout my book, I'm going to speak with you on a one-to-one basis, just as I devote myself to each and every one of the clients I treat in my salon. I want to reach you in that same personal way. I don't conduct my business on a mass scale, seeing as many clients as I can in one day. I deal with people and their individual needs, not overfilled appointment books.

I'm going to explain all of my techniques and give you the "how, what, and why" of everything I do because I want you to understand the reasoning that exists behind all facets of skin care. I have one aim in mind: to help you help yourself to a more perfect skin, something that every woman and man deserves and can have.

You're on a new path to skin beauty. Let's take the first step together.

2

Which Skin Type Are You?

Your skin is a reflection of you. It is the first aspect of you that another person notices and it is a great revealer. If your skin looks blemished, fatigued, or sallow, it not only detracts from your appearance, but it also says that you are not taking care of yourself properly. Let's face facts: we are living in a time when looking good is imperative. In our busy, hectic life, other people may not take the time to look past a problem complexion to the person struggling underneath. I know that this sounds harsh, but it is true. On the other hand, if your skin has a special clarity and glow, you look alive and exciting, with a refreshing vitality that everyone will respond to.

Skin, and that aspect of it we call the complexion, can be your greatest glory, expressing the idealization and refinement of feminine beauty.

Fine skin is the face's poetry, exquisite, beautiful, complex. Every woman can achieve this perfection.

Beautiful skin is always desired and appreciated by you and those around you. But before it can be beautiful, it must be understood. More than your body's greatest organ, more than a protective layer, your skin is as different and as individual as you are. To understand your complexion and its individual problems and personality, you must learn to analyze your skin.

Analysis☞　**Understanding**☞　**Appreciation**

A SIMPLE TEST

Determining the quality of your skin is where beauty begins. All you need is a mirror.

I want you to take a good, critical look at yourself. I want to hear what *you* think of your skin. Your face must be clean, without a trace of makeup or soil. With your mirror in your hand, find the sunniest spot in your home; natural light is the most honest and you don't want to hide in shadows anymore.

Be truthful in your assessment of your complexion: don't look for excuses. Look up at your forehead . . . let your eyes travel down the length of your nose to your chin . . . turn to each cheek and then focus straight into the mirror for an overall view.

Check one of the following statements, the one that most accurately describes you:

★ My skin is dull: my pores are congested; the color and tone of my skin is poor; it's not as elastic as it should be. Help!

★ My skin is average: it's good, but not good enough. My face lacks that special glow that says, "Hey, notice me." I don't get many compliments.

★ My skin is superlative: my face is alive and radiant; my skin is almost translucent. What a complexion!

The superlative skin is every woman's dream, but it isn't enough to have it—you must also learn how to maintain it. This is your total goal, one you can reach once you know exactly what type of skin you have.

THE BARE FACTS

Let's look beneath the surface for a moment, to understand your skin, what it's made of and what roles it must carry out.

Skin is composed of two distinct strata: the DERMIS and the EPIDERMIS.

The *dermis* is the bottom strata, the skin's activity center. The dermis is often called the *true skin* because its condition is what determines whether the epidermis is oily, dry, or balanced. Within the dermis are located the capillaries or blood vessels which bring the skin oxygen, its vital nourishment. Also present are the sebaceous or oil glands which deliver the necessary lubricants to the epidermis, keeping it soft and supple, and the sudoriferous or sweat glands whose secretions help our body maintain its correct temperature.

The *epidermis* is the visible strata of skin. This outer layer is often called the *scarf cuticle* because it protects the skin's other, underlying layers. The outermost cells of the epidermis form an overlapping, waterproof covering which enables it to accomplish that job. In the normal process of growth, these cells flake off imperceptibly. This sloughing is nature's way of ridding the skin of dead cells, making room for the new ones to rise from the dermis.

PERFECT SKIN: THE pH FACTOR

A beautiful, healthy skin is one that has a perfect balance. It is a skin that secretes just the right amount of oil (fatty acids). If there is too much oil, the skin becomes oily; too little and it becomes dry. The pH factor measures the concentration of fatty acids and alkalines on the skin surface. A balance must exist between the fatty acids and the alkalines or salts that also reach the scarf cuticle. If the fatty acids are excessive, making your skin oily, they must be neutralized with alkalines. Alkalines have a drying effect on your skin. For those with dry skin, the alkalines must be compensated with fatty acids or oil. Balanced skin can do this by itself.

If your skin is not perfect, you're probably wondering why this is so. Why was I singled out? you might be asking.

We were all born with fine, balanced skin, but the baby-soft quality of our young skin isn't permanent. As we mature, our skin changes. Its quality and characteristics programmed in our genes, passed on to us by our parents and our ancestors, begin to show themselves. Whether we like it or not, whether our adult skin is oily or dry or balanced has all been predetermined. But that doesn't mean we can't better the quality or phelityl (pH) of our skin. It does require work, but it can be done. The pH or perfect balance of your skin is not a chance occurrence and, more importantly, you can't leave your skin to chance.

MY SKIN SCALE AND YOUR SKIN TYPE

I don't believe in categorizing a person's skin as "normal" or "oily" or "dry." Determining your skin type is never as elementary as a-b-c. Though skins which are oily have some common denominators, as do skins which are dry, there are various degrees of oiliness, and dryness. Even a balanced skin might not be 100 per cent balanced; certain balanced skins may have a tendency to become slightly dry and others, in rare instances, slightly oily.

This is why I developed my own system of pinpointing that individual type of skin that is yours. My *Skin Scale* tips, on one side, toward the dry skins and, on the other, to the oily skins.

Because an oily skin secretes an excess amount of oil, I call it a PLUS skin.

Because a dry skin secretes an insufficient amount of oil, I call it a MINUS skin.

The *Skin Scale* measures the severity of both the PLUS (+) and the MINUS (−) skins on a scale of 1 to 4, from the mildest case to the most severe.

A BALANCED skin is smooth, soft, supple. Skin is healthy and glowing. It has a marvelous elasticity which insures its suppleness. This skin can expand and easily regain its shape after a laugh, a smile. This is a quality which must be preserved, improved, and abetted at all times.

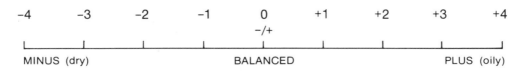

THE JANET SARTIN SKIN SCALE

BALANCED SKIN

Does your skin feel soft?
Is your skin free of shine?
Is your face free of blemishes and clogged pores?

If your answer to each of these questions is YES, you're a very lucky person, with a fantastic complexion.

A BALANCED skin is generally free of the shine and the blemishes of a PLUS skin, free of the tautness of a MINUS skin. Your nose area may secrete more oil than you would like, but this is sometimes true of even a dry skin—this is a natural function that insures the protection of this all-important organ.

BALANCED skin, represented on my scale by 0, has an added −/+ variant to signal that you must always be on your guard against tipping to either side of the scale.

PLUS SKIN: THE OILY COMPLEXION

The PLUS or oily skin is subject to an overload of oils, so much so that excesses can harden in pores, forming blackheads. Skin becomes sluggish, losing elasticity as pores become too clogged to function properly. If new oils that rise to the epidermis as lubrication are not exuded, they can become trapped and form blemishes or pimples. In some cases, the skin can lapse into folds and crevices under the weight of these excess secretions, forming lines and wrinkles or furrows.

We are in a breakthrough or breakout situation: oil must break through the clogged pore barrier or else you will suffer a breakout of blemishes and we all know how disastrous that can be!

Blackheads are all the fault of overproductive sebaceous glands. These secrete more sebum or oil than is needed to maintain a healthy, supple complexion. The excesses collect in little sacs of fluid that open onto hair follicles or pores. To worsen this blockage, the ingestion of certain foods sets up a further irritation. They contain substances that leave your body through your pores. If pores are clogged, these other secretions won't be able to break through to the surface and more blemishes form, along with a reddening of the skin, the result of the strain to pass the oil barrier.

In extreme cases, pustules and boils form, erupting like icebergs in the dermis. These should never be squeezed because you may only reach the surface problem. The infection that would then remain underneath could fester and become reinfected, turning into the more complicated problem of a lesion or scar.

The PLUS skin is fortunately not always a blemished skin. If the excess oil is fluid enough to reach the skin surface, you may not have a crucial blockage problem. You may only have a persistent shine. But this is not to say that you should ignore this or any other problem. Problems that are ignored become intensified; they don't disappear as we would like.

Before I tell you about the four different degrees of oiliness, let me pose a few questions which will help you identify your skin type. After you have read each of the following descriptions, turn back to these questions and your answers.

You will see that there are four choices for each question; the first choice indicates the mildest degree of oiliness, the fourth, the most severe. Count how many questions you answered with the first choice, the second, the third, and then the fourth. The most prevalent will be the key to determining whether you have a +1, a +2, a +3, or a +4 complexion.

a. Rate your skin's oilness: during the day, does your face acquire

★ a light shine, just a bit more than a glow?

★ a heavy shine, like an oily film?

★ a very heavy coating that is occlusive?

★ a mask so greasy your face never feels clean?

b. Are your pores

★ clogged and enlarged?

★ blocked by blackheads and company to blemishes?

★ no longer pores but bumps under your skin?

★ you don't notice pores because of infectious eruptions such as pustules and boils?

c. Do you have blemishes

★ rarely?

★ occasionally?

★ often?

★ constantly?

As you read on, remember that every problem skin can be helped, once you recognize the problem.

THE +1 SKIN

This skin has a tendency to tip to the PLUS side of the scale.

Your nose area is prone to blackheads. Conversely, the area around the eyes, the upper lip area, and the neck tend to be dry, requiring a different kind of care. In some cases, these areas can be involved in the oily situation, prone to enlarged, clogged pores and blemishes.

The skin care program for this skin type is described in chapter 3, "The World's Best (and Simplest) Skin Care System."

THE +2 SKIN

This skin has too much of a good thing—those lubricating oils. The sebaceous glands are more active than they should be. Your skin acquires a light shine.

Enlarged pores turn into a major source of discontent; they expand as plugs or blackheads form and harden. You may have to contend with an occasional pimple or two as well.

Conversely, the area around the eyes, the upper lip area, and the neck tend to be dry, requiring a different kind of care. In some cases, these areas can be involved in the oily situation, prone to enlarged, clogged pores and blackheads.

The skin care program for this skin type is described in chapter 3, "The World's Best (and Simplest) Skin Care System."

THE +3 SKIN

As my clients often say, this skin rarely feels clean! Oily secretions are not being evenly distributed to your epidermis. Blackheads and blemishes are a common occurrence, particularly in the form of spot breakouts.

At times you have a very emotional

complexion, one which reacts with your moods, your ups and downs. The excess oiliness can play havoc with your emotions all by itself. The additional stress and anxiety that stem from having this type of skin can turn into a nasty cycle: blemishes increase because of your anxiety, in turn creating more blemishes. You might not be taking the proper steps in skin care; you might be eating foods that cause an adverse reaction on your face.

Unlike the rest of your face, the area around your eyes, the upper lip area, and the neck might be subject to dryness and therefore would require a different kind of care. In some cases, these areas can be involved in the oily situation, prone to enlarged, clogged pores and blackheads.

Read chapter 3, "The World's Best (and Simplest) Skin Care System," for a description of the preparations you'll be using. Then turn to chapter 5, "Problem Skin: Breakthrough or Breakout," for the specific program for your skin.

THE +4 SKIN

This skin is most perplexing, though not beyond help. There are many factors involved—stress and diet, for example—which can aggravate an oily skin condition. Most assuredly, though, you have an excessive amount of lubricating oils stemming from your sebaceous glands creating blemishes and infections, possibly postules and/or boils that redden and mar the skin surface. Acne is present and you must learn how to treat it.

Your skin can become sluggish, overpowered by the excessive oils and the resultant fatty accumulations or lumps that fester under the surface.

Conversely, the area around your eyes, the upper lip area, and the neck tend to be dry, requiring a different type of care. In some cases, these areas can be involved in the oily situation, prone to enlarged, clogged pores and blackheads.

Read chapter 3, "The World's Best (and Simplest) Skin Care System," for a description of the preparations you'll be using. Then turn to chapter 5, "Problem Skin: Breakthrough or Breakout," for the specific program for your skin.

MINUS SKIN: THE DRY COMPLEXION

As I explained previously, there are four degrees of dryness. It isn't always simple to figure out for yourself which is the real you. To help you determine the degree of dryness of your skin, I am going to give you some questions to think over.

When you've finished reading this section, turn back to the questions and your answers. The first choice for each question applies to the −1 skin, the last to the −4 or most severe MINUS skin. Count how many questions you answered with the first choice, the second, the third, and then the fourth. The most frequently chosen answer will be the key to determining whether you have a −1, a −2, a −3, or a −4 complexion.

a.   Rate your skin's dryness: does your skin feel
★   dry?
★   very dry?
★   uncomfortably taut?
★   rough and parched?

b.   Do you have specific areas of dryness
★   above your upper lip, under your eyes, and on your neck?
★   *and* your cheeks?
★   all-over dryness?
★   your face feels like a desert!

c.   Do you notice fine wrinkling
★   around your eyes?
★   *and* the corners of your mouth?
★   on your forehead as well?
★   overall wrinkling and crevicing?

d.   Is your complexion affected by
★   a change in season?
★   yes, it gets *much* drier when the seasons change.
★   yes, it chaps in the winter, burns easily in the sun.
★   you're afraid to go out at all!

You may think that some of these possible answers are too funny to be serious. Well, that is because I don't want you to be scared away by the truth, which can often come as a shock to your psyche. It is true that you must care for your face seriously, but remember, at the same time, that caring is positive, constructive, and beneficial therapy and that the results it brings will make you happy. But if you approach skin care with an attitude of hopelessness, you'll only succeed in defeating your purpose.

Understanding your skin will help you see it in a more hopeful light, so let me tell you about your skin type and, in the next chapters, what you can do about correcting its problems.

Your skin feels dry because your natural supply of lubricating oil falls below the minimum daily requirement it needs to stay supple, elastic, healthy. Too little oil reaches your skin surface and, as a result, your skin is prone to wrinkling, chapping, cracking, and simply feeling uncomfortable. This can cause it to age more rapidly.

The MINUS skin hasn't the oil supply (or moisture supply, as it is often called) to insure the suppleness needed for the release of expression lines made when you pout or smile, to name only two emotions you readily show through your face. These lines can deepen and become permanent—I will be telling you how to prevent this in later chapters.

MINUS skin cannot suffer exposure to the elements. It cannot renew itself after the harsh sunburning it gets in the summer and the chapping cold that attacks in the winter. MINUS skin feels taut year-round, worse often after the simple act of washing it, if that is done incorrectly.

Skin can absorb only a minimum amount of cream through its outer layers; MINUS skin is even more resistant. Yet it can be helped, once you are aware of the extent of the dryness.

THE −1 SKIN

This skin has a tendency to become occasionally dry. Your skin is not always as supple and as soft as you would like it to be.

Unlike the rest of your face, the

nose area may secrete oils and be subject to enlarged, clogged pores and, consequently, blackheads.

The skin care program for this skin type is described in chapter 3, "The World's Best (and Simplest) Skin Care System."

THE −2 SKIN

This skin is dry; your face feels taut when you touch it. Extreme weather conditions show readily on your face. Your skin hasn't enough natural means to fight the cold or the sun, both of which elements can easily dry your skin further.

Your skin has a tendency to wrinkle because the epidermis is not well lubricated and hasn't the suppleness it needs to release expression lines. You need additional protection to compensate for the lack of natural oils.

Conversely, your nose area may secrete oils and be subject to enlarged, clogged pores and, consequently, blackheads.

The skin care program for this skin type is described in chapter 3, "The World's Best (and Simplest) Skin Care System."

THE −3 SKIN

This skin always feels uncomfortable, signaling a serious problem. It needs constant care because the oil glands are highly underactive. Without additional lubrication, your skin won't be pliant or soft. Your skin reacts very adversely to changes in temperature. Special attention will first be given to correct this condition and then to maintain the newfound softness.

Conversely, your nose, which may secrete oil, might require a different kind of care.

Read chapter 3, "The World's Best (and Simplest) Skin Care System," for a description of the preparations you'll be using. Then turn to chapter 7, "Approaching the Vintage Years," for the specific program for your skin.

THE −4 SKIN

This is the extreme dry skin condition. The chemistry of the body and the skin acts almost as a censor, stymieing the normal secretion of oils that your skin needs for its well-being.

Your skin has little chance of helping itself: the −4 condition is acute. There is no suppleness to your skin and, consequently, expression lines become deeply embedded.

The problem is often worsened by prolonged exposure to the sun. The sports enthusiast and the sun worshipper who insists on getting that deep, dark tan every summer will soon find themselves not only with taut facial skin, but with premature wrinkling as well.

Conversely, your nose, which may secrete oil, might require a different kind of care.

Read chapter 3, "The World's Best (and Simplest) Skin Care System," for a description of the preparations you'll be using. Then turn to chapter 7, "Approaching the Vintage Years," for the specific program for your skin.

COMPLEX COMPLEXIONS

There are certain complex skin problems that don't fall into any of the PLUS or MINUS groupings.

THE T-ZONE CORRECTIVE SKIN

By now you know that the nose area is often prone to excess oiliness, clogged pores and, consequently, blackheads. On some skins, this oiliness can extend directly upward to the forehead and downward to the chin.

This three-part area is known as the T-zone, the forehead making up the horizontal bar of the letter "T" and the

nose and the chin its vertical axis. The PLUS areas however might only comprise the nose and the chin or the nose and the forehead.

If all the other areas of your face are balanced, you have a BALANCED SKIN WITH A T-ZONE CORRECTIVE, so called because the T-zone area needs corrective skin care. You will use the BALANCED skin care system described in the next chapter, extending the use of astringent based products (used on the nose) to the forehead and/or chin as needed.

THE COMBINATION SKIN

This skin type is often difficult to determine because, on the surface, your skin feels dry; in fact, it is parched. The oiliness that you have (and thought you had outgrown) is in hiding, beneath the skin surface. In essence, this is still an oily or PLUS skin with the complication of a dry or parched scarf cuticle.

A COMBINATION skin can result from various situations. If you tried to dry out your oily skin with abrasive products and succeeded in drying only the skin surface, your skin condition is the result of improper care.

If you are a compulsive tanner, a sports enthusiast whose oily skin has been overexposed to the sun and now feels dry to the touch, overexposure without the necessary precautions is the cause.

You may notice as well bumps under the surface that are actually fatty deposits. These deposits are hardened oils that became trapped under the parched layer, unable to rise to the surface—your oily skin condition has not disappeared. Rather, the oil is imprisoned, unable to break through to the layer of parched skin.

It is easy to mistake this skin type for dry skin, but treating it as such would only worsen the problem—too much cream would only further block the pores with oil. Remember that the key to identifying this COMBINATION skin is the presence of subsurface bumps that occur with a parched scarf cuticle—these accumulations do not occur with a truly dry skin.

Read chapter 3, "The World's Best (and Simplest) Skin Care System," for a description of the preparations you'll be using. Then turn to chapter 5, "Problem Skin: Breakthrough or Breakout," for the specific program for your skin.

THE SENSITIVE SKIN

A SENSITIVE skin can be an emotional skin that reacts to certain foods or medications as well as stress. This skin can develop a reddish pinpoint irritation or other prickly type rash.

A SENSITIVE skin is not usually an oily or PLUS skin and therefore, once desensitized, can be treated as a BALANCED complexion. Through the consistent use of the proper preparations, this skin can be made to resist sensitive reactions.

Read chapter 3, "The World's Best (and Simplest) Skin Care System," for a description of the preparations you'll be using. Then turn to chapter 5, "Problem Skin: Breakthrough or Breakout," for the specific program for your skin.

THE ALLERGIC SKIN

The ALLERGIC skin presents a constant problem. It will break out into either hives or another form of irritation due to the ingestion of certain foods such as strawberries or those with a high mineral content (i.e., shellfish).

It can also be affected by the use of a preparation such as a makeup formulated with iridescence or a cream based product.

The ALLERGIC skin must be treated like a +1 skin in order to draw out the inflammation and therefore strengthen it.

Read chapter 3, "The World's Best (and Simplest) Skin Care System," for a description of the preparations you'll be using. Then turn to chapter 5, "Problem Skin: Breakthrough or Breakout," for the specific program for your skin.

In the next chapters, I will help you out of this and all the other skin problems I have described.

Skin is a fantastic organ and, if handled properly, will give you anything that you ask of it, without drastic measures.

Once you have determined your specific skin type, we can go on to the proper care needed to turn it from dull to average, from average to superlative. And superlative is perfect.

3.

The World's Best (and Simplest) Skin Care System.

Beautiful skin is both achieved and maintained with the proper care. Cleansing your face is a great part of this care and accomplishing the job requires careful thought. Buying a highly advertised bar of soap at the supermarket will not work for you. It might be fine for the girl you saw promoting it on a commercial, but remember that using the "pure, natural" soap didn't get her that job—being born (very luckily) with beautiful skin did.

Most soaps won't harm a balanced skin, but won't help a PLUS or MINUS skin that needs benefits from every preparation you use. You cannot expect a hand or deodorant soap to do the job of one specially formulated for your skin type.

If you have a PLUS skin, you need a soap that will help reduce the oiliness on your skin surface and guard against harmful bacteria.

If you have BALANCED or MINUS skin, you need a soap that will work to increase your skin's suppleness.

By using cleansing preparations designed for *your* skin, you can look more healthy and natural than the girl who claims to use just any bar of soap and water.

I want you to know that I am talking to both men and women, here and throughout my book. Today it is more important than ever for a man's skin to look and feel good, especially if the man is in the highly competitive business world where appearance can make all the difference in success. Once a man is sure of himself, he can face life with a greater sense of confidence. There's no reason why we all shouldn't experience that wonderful feeling that comes from knowing we are attractive.

THE pH BUSINESS

Before I begin telling you about the various preparations you will be using, I would like to say a few definitive words on the subject of your phelityl (pH) balance. The pH balance is the perfect balance between acidity and alkalinity on your skin surface. Misled by packaging and advertising, consumers imagine that their skin care products should be pH balanced, too. A whole industry seems to have sprung up around the use of testing papers, scraps that turn colors when dipped in the products.

Well, when I'm developing a product, I don't look for a formula that will turn paper blue or green or gold. I search for a product that will work, the strongest statement any preparation can make and one most of those on today's market cannot. The pH factor refers to our skin, and you're going to want to use the product that will help your skin achieve that perfection. So if you have PLUS skin, for example, you will want an alkaline product to balance the fatty acids. As you use it to remove the excess oils, you're going to be thinking about the pores that are becoming unclogged, not about which color the test paper might turn.

MINUS SKIN

FOREHEAD

CHEEKS

CHIN

CORRECTION THROUGH CLEANSING

When planning your cleansing routine, your skin type must be your primary consideration; it dictates the *what,* the *how,* and the *when.* You must also take into account certain distinct areas of your face which may need different care.

For example, if you have PLUS skin, your nose will naturally be oily as well. But the person with MINUS skin will wonder why the nose is oily when the rest of the face feels dry. The oiliness of this area is nature's way of protecting it from extreme cold or heat. Often, the forehead and the chin which, in addition to the nose, comprise the T-zone are oily as well. If the nose or T-zone is oily, yet the rest of your face is dry, you will take additional cleansing steps to correct both situations.

Conversely, if you have a PLUS skin, you may wonder why you feel dryness around your eyes, upper lip, and neck. It is because these areas do not receive enough natural oil to supplement the effects of the daily loss of moisture.

Just as the nose is oily for *almost* everyone, the eye area, the upper lip area, and the neck are dry for *almost* everyone. Almost is the important word here because there is always an exception. A very oily situation might carry over to the usually dry areas. A very dry, —4 skin can include the nose.

Make sure you are aware of the distinct skin types your complexion reveals.

THE PREPARATIONS

I believe in preparations that do a specific job for your skin. That may seem elementary, but if you take a look at the products that claim to be beneficial, you'll understand how easily one can be misled by promises.

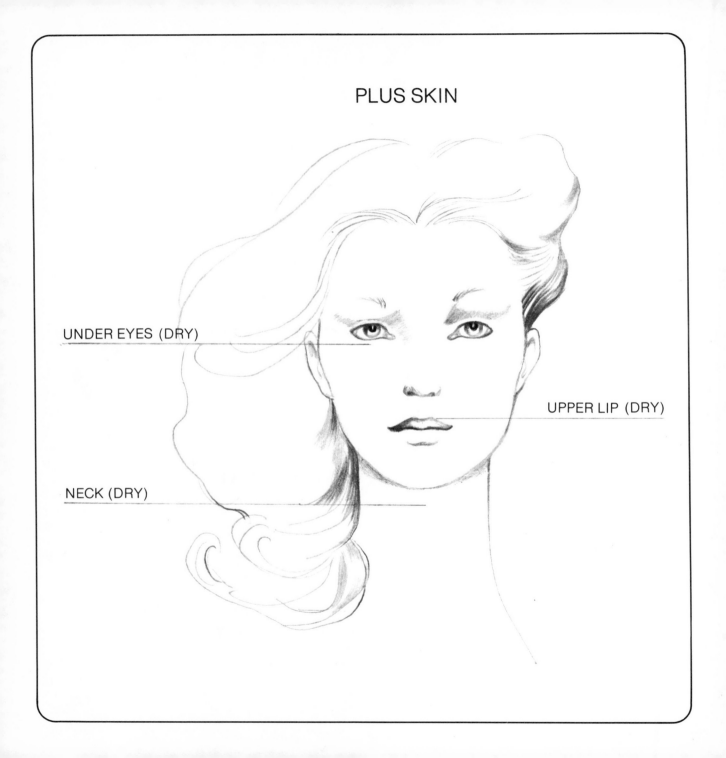

Battery-operated skin brushes and scrubbers are well-advertised commodities. But what you don't hear about in the promotions is how they can strip your face of its natural oils. Buffers, abrasive cleaning pads, exfoliating and peeling preparations are all harmful. Your skin naturally sloughs off all the "dead cells" by itself. There's nothing to gain by subjecting it to these artificial, sensitizing procedures. You want to care for your skin; you don't want to traumatize it.

With the proper preparations, a PLUS skin can correct itself and a MINUS skin can be kept happy and comfortable.

My two-step system involves first taking off the day's dirt and makeup—*cleansing* your skin—and, secondly, giving it a *treatment* bath with a soap designed for it. I have found that the benefits of ingredients incorporated in soap can be increased by using it as a treatment rather than a simple wash. Your face is lathered and then rinsed with the same rich water contained in your basin, aerating your skin, making it come alive.

PLUS SKIN SYSTEM PREPARATIONS

Astringent cleanses all the oily areas of your face, the nose in particular. A good astringent should have a 45 per cent alcohol content, formulated with distilled water. You don't want a freshener or toner whose alcohol content would be too low, nor do you want a rubbing alcohol which would not be well enough refined. Look for a fragrance-free product designed for oily skin. CLEAR ASTRINGENT is the cleansing lotion I developed, the first step in the corrective treatment. It prepares the skin for the second cleansing step: the soap treatment.

Anti-bacterial, anti-acne soap is designed for the PLUS skin. You'll want to look carefully for those two phrases when you buy your soap. Don't search through cosmetic counters—you don't want a fragrance soap. Check the medicated soap section of your pharmacy. My soap is called 1012 SOAP because it was designed to offer you a minimum of ten to twelve hours of protection. Its special formula helps thin out the thickened oils so that they may flow more easily from the pores, encouraging the skin to rid itself of impurities.

WHITE ASTRINGENT is a preparation I developed to act as an overnight treatment to free pores of sluggish oils and help the skin achieve a better balance. This bedtime treatment can be quite flattering. The lightly powdered finish that remains on the skin after the lotion has been applied and blotted gives the skin a pretty bloom. It is especially soothing for men who are prone to shaving irritations. The many uses of this preparation are also discussed in chapter 5, "Problem Skin: Breakthrough or Breakout."

BALANCED AND MINUS SKIN SYSTEM PREPARATIONS

A mineral oil complex is the cleansing material I recommend for BALANCED to dry skins. I don't advise a cream for cleansing because you would have to work both the cream and the underlying dirt into the skin before both the preparation and the soil could be removed. Creams will be used as treatments after the cleansing and soap bath. A good cleansing oil complex must be a well-refined combination of various oils, a mineral oil *plus* a peanut or sesame oil. Baby oil won't nourish or lubricate dry, mature skin satisfactorily. Check the list of ingredients on the label for a better formulated product. My preparation, called simply CLEANSING OIL, is formulated from the richest oils available. Its light texture leaves a water soluble oily film on your skin to create an emulsion when followed with the soap treatment.

A fatty acid based soap is needed to soften the scarf cuticle. A glycerine type soap is not sufficient. The ingredients to look for are lanolin, fatty acids, or oils. My SUPERFATTED SOAP, when used in conjunction with oil, as described above, works to restore the fatty acids necessary to make your skin healthy and smooth.

Nourishing cream is the additional treatment for the BALANCED or dry skin. You need a light-textured cream that works in five to fifteen minutes. You don't want a moisturizer that will lie heavily on your face. The preparation I developed is called SUPERFATTED CREAM. It is a light-textured silken cream that is easily blotted off for a greaseless feeling of comfort.

THE BASIC TOOLS
FOR ALL SKINS

Clean hands. Be sure your hands are clean before you begin. When using the soap as a treatment, I recommend washing and rinsing with hands, never a washcloth which could spread bacteria.

Cotton. Buy a roll of sterilized cotton which permits you to take only the amount you need as you need it. Cotton balls are often too small and too difficult to reshape to get the maximum usage from all four sides. You can be very thrifty by turning it inside out after you have used the two outsides.

Cotton can be separated into thin layers for beauty compresses as described in other chapters, as well as a variety of other needs.

Store the roll in a container of its own, perhaps an attractive glass jar.

A clean basin or bowl for the soap and water treatment is a must.

THE PLUS
SKIN SYSTEM

In the morning and evening, before dressing:

1. Saturate a piece of sterilized cotton with astringent (CLEAR ASTRINGENT) and gently cleanse your face, omitting the area around your eyes, the upper lip area, and the neck, if these are dry and unblemished. First cleanse the nose area, then, changing the cotton, move to one cheek, then to the other and down around your chin. Move to the center of your forehead between the eyebrows and first cleanse the area to the right, then the left, including the outer eye area to the hairline if it is subject to enlarged, clogged pores (if not, include this area in step 2).

Use fresh cotton as needed until it stays clean.

2. Saturate a clean piece of cotton with a mineral oil complex (CLEANSING OIL) and cleanse the area around your eyes, the upper lip, and the neck if they are dry and not subject to clogged, enlarged pores and blemishes.

3. Fill your basin or bowl with warm water—never hot or cold, as extremes can cause breakage of fragile capillaries, a condition which is difficult to remedy. Wet your face and hands. Lather your face with your wet anti-bacterial, anti-acne soap (1012 SOAP) and make a separate lather in your hands. Work the lathers gently into your skin.

4. Holding your elbows out to the sides, rinse your face with the water in the basin for a total of *fifteen* times to derive the full treatment benefits of the soap and water aeration. Brisk, bracing splashes remove any final traces of soil, leaving the skin flawlessly clean without a taut, dry feeling.

5. Dry your face and neck with a clean, soft towel.

6. Follow with the makeup steps outlined in chapter 4, "Making Makeup Work for You."

In the evening, before retiring, remove your lipstick and eye makeup as described below and then follow the morning routine through step 5. Continue with:

6. Saturate a clean piece of cotton with my well-shaken WHITE ASTRINGENT and apply to your face, omitting the area around your eyes, the upper lip area, and the neck, if these are dry. To remove any excess, blot gently in a smoothing motion.

Blotting is easily done with a tissue wrapped around your first two fingers.

7. Smooth a light, nourishing cream (SUPERFATTED CREAM) under the eyes, above the upper lip area, and on the neck, if these areas are dry. Leave it on for *ten* minutes. Gently wipe off with a tissue.

PRELUDE TO NIGHTTIME CLEANSING FOR PLUS, BALANCED, AND MINUS SKIN

Lipstick and Eye Makeup Removal

Both your lipstick and your eye makeup—shadow, mascara, liner—should be removed before your last cleansing of the day begins.

Let's start with your lips:

1. Saturate a clean piece of cotton with a mineral oil complex (CLEANSING OIL). Start at the outer corner of your upper lip and cleanse to the center, first from the right corner, then from the left for a swift removal. Turn the cotton over and repeat. Turn the cotton inside out and cleanse your lower lip.

2. Using a tissue, blot your lips, again moving from the outer corners in.

NOTE: If you are subject to enlarged, clogged pores and blackheads along the upper or lower lipline, treat these areas with well-shaken WHITE ASTRINGENT before retiring.

I would like to suggest an easy way of removing your eye makeup—mascara in particular—one that least traumatizes your eyes while it helps keep your lashes lush and luxurious.

(SEE THE FOLLOWING PAGES)

1. Dip both ends of a cotton swab in a mineral oil complex (CLEANSING OIL). Place a single-ply tissue under your lower lashes, against the skin. Using one end of the swab at a time, brush both the top and the underside of your upper lashes, rotating the swab as you stroke for maximum use. Always hold the tissue in place as it prevents the mascara from smearing on your skin and blots any oil which could blur your eyes.

2. Repeat the procedure for the lower lashes. Change swabs as needed until all mascara is removed.

3. Once the mascara is removed, gently fold the tissue over your lashes and smooth away all traces of oil. Repeat as needed.

4. Eye shadow and liner—what little might remain after the above steps—can be easily removed with a saturated swab or cotton.

THE BALANCED AND MINUS SKIN SYSTEM

NOTE: Because the BALANCED skin can have a tendency to lose its natural oils as it matures, it should be kept on this program designed for dry skin. But if, on the other hand, this skin veers to oiliness, it should be placed on the plus system and treated as a +1 skin.

In the morning and evening, before dressing:

1. Saturate a piece of sterilized cotton with a mineral oil complex (CLEANSING OIL) and gently cleanse your face, omitting your nose, as it is usually subject to enlarged, clogged pores. Cleanse the right side of your face first, using a sweeping movement from the inner corner of the eye extending outward over the cheek and jaw area. Use the reverse side of the cotton and then turn it inside out. Repeat this for the left side of your face. Move to the center of your forehead and cleanse to the right, then to the left. Saturate clean cotton and go across the chin. Cleanse the neck from the center to the right and then the center to the left.

Use fresh cotton as needed until clean. Do not blot.

2. Saturate a clean piece of cotton with astringent (CLEAR ASTRINGENT) and cleanse the nose, being sure to clean in the curve of the nostrils and beneath the tip.

3. Fill your basin or bowl with warm water—never hot or cold as extremes can cause breakage of fragile capillaries, a condition which is difficult to remedy. Wet your face and hands. Lather your face with your wet fatty acid based soap (SUPERFATTED SOAP) and make a separate lather in your hands. Work both lathers gently into your skin. With the oil residue, this soap creates an emulsion to soften your skin.

4. Holding your elbows out to the sides, rinse your face with the water in the basin for a total of *fifteen* times to derive the full treatment benefits of the emulsion.

5. Dry your face and neck with a clean, soft towel.

6. Smooth a light nourishing cream (SUPERFATTED CREAM) on your face and neck, omitting the nose, as it is usually subject to enlarged, clogged pores. Leave it on for *five* minutes. Gently wipe off the excess with a tissue and blot in this manner:

Place a tissue over the area; using your fingertips, smooth it against your skin. Lift it off.

7. Follow with the makeup steps outlined in chapter 4, "Making Makeup Work for You."

In the evening, before retiring, remove your lipstick and eye makeup as described above and follow the morning routine through step 6, leaving the cream on your skin for a total of *fifteen* minutes. Continue with:

8. Saturate a clean piece of cotton with my well-shaken WHITE ASTRINGENT and apply it to your nose and blot with a tissue wrapped around your first two fingers. This treatment will help free pores and reduce excess oiliness that ordinary astringent will not.

CONSISTENCY

I believe in spending the shortest amount of time possible as effectively as you can. For the BALANCED and MINUS skins, twice-a-day cleansing is enough if you follow the routine faithfully. If you are a —1 or —2 and feel uncomfortable, you might want to give yourself an additional treatment during the day. Also, you should never leave your face bare if you are venturing outside, if for only a moment. If you should see someone you know and smile to them, you want to know that there is a preparation on your face that will help ease those expression lines back into place. If your home is heated, you'll want to know your face is protected from that element as well.

The +1 and +2 skins should follow their program a minimum of twice a day, preferably three. If you are not able to practice the routine midday, yet notice excess oiliness, you may blot the oily areas with a tissue and reapply face powder as explained in chapter 4, "Making Makeup Work for You." For those who can practice the routine midday, at the office, outfit yourself with a few small plastic bottles, the travel-size kind that can fit into your purse. Be ready to devote a small part of your lunch hour to cleansing your face and reapplying your makeup. The results will be worth it. With a few weeks of consistent care, both the +2 and the −2 skin can, in many cases, become a +1 and a −1 skin respectively, conditions that can be controlled with your morning and nighttime routine alone.

I haven't encumbered the cleansing systems with a variety of products you would never remember to use. The facial sauna is an example of a skin-cleansing apparatus that many have been told they need. I find it totally unnecessary and have found that, in the long run, it can do more harm than good. The steam involved debilitates the skin, slowing down its natural processes by opening the pores. I want to *activate* your skin by renewing its cycles, not reducing them. For MINUS skins especially these machines are to be avoided as they can create more wrinkles. The very mention of them evokes in my mind the image of an old woman whose shriveled face looks dangerously reminiscent of a prune.

Don't look for obstacles when you approach the cleansing of your face. If you keep the routine simple, you will adhere to it—and that is a must. My program is one that will give you results every day, accumulative results that accrue as the days pass. But I want a firm commitment from you because you are the one person who can control your complexion.

Your hair can influence the condition of your skin. If your hair has a tendency to be oily, by all means keep it off your face. Choose a style that encourages your hair to fall away from your face, not a cut that causes the ends to touch your cheeks or jawline where light hair fuzz has a pre-tendency to clog pores. Oil from your hair will mix with the oils on your face to cause an irritation or blemish.

If your hair is excessively oily, be sure to wash it every day or every other day.

Keep your scalp clean and healthy. If you have a flaky scalp condition, take the necessary steps to remedy the problem. Follow my suggestions in chapter 8, "Body Essentials"; it will not disappear on its own.

Keep your hair preparations from touching your skin. Hair spray especially can irritate any type of skin.

CORRECT

CORRECT

YOUR OWN PRIVATE CORNER

Your essentials should be kept neatly in an area of your bathroom that's yours alone. Of course, we aren't all lucky enough to have an entire bathroom to ourselves and, if you share with a husband, wife, or roommate, you might want to get your own bowl and pitcher for your soap treatment. You won't have to bother with the bathroom basin at all.

I keep all my preparations on a tray with a separate container for my sterilized cotton and, even more importantly, a place for my soap all its own. That's the one sure way to keep the other members of your family from using it, although I must say that in one instance a shared soap turned out to be a very good thing.

Freddie Brisson, husband of the late Rosalind Russell, has a most sensitive complexion. One day, he found his wife's bar of SUPERFATTED SOAP and began using it. He discovered it to be the only soap he was ever able to use comfortably and has used it ever since for its great soothing properties!

CHECKLIST

YOUR CLEANSING ESSENTIALS PREPARATIONS AND TOOLS

A 45 per cent alcohol astringent for the PLUS areas.

A mineral oil complex for the BALANCED and MINUS areas.

An anti-bacterial, anti-acne soap for the PLUS skin only.

A fatty acid based soap for the BALANCED and MINUS skins only.

WHITE ASTRINGENT for the PLUS areas.

A nourishing cream for the BALANCED and MINUS areas.

Sterilized cotton and optional storage container.

Cotton swabs.

Tissues.

4

Making Makeup Work for You

When I talk about makeup, I am not referring to a foundation or a base, both of which words must be eliminated from your cosmetic dictionary. Only corrective, protective, and preventive preparations are allowed. Clear, healthy skin that glows is the only canvas upon which grooming aids or cosmetics should be applied. A troubled complexion should never be coated with a heavy makeup, which would, in fact, only compound the problem. Makeup should only be used to enhance your appearance and, as I will explain, to aid and abet a lustrous, silky complexion.

Before I discuss the various preparations you will be using, I want you to look in your mirror and tell me what you see. Does your expression reflect a happy disposition or is it a reflection of inner stress? Do your expression lines show anger, impatience, or annoyance with those around you? Any kind of negative stress will cause your face to droop downward, robbing you of the natural uplift of a spiritually contented person.

If you're not sure of what a serene expression is, why not take a look at the Mona Lisa, the world's most beloved painting? Notice her ever-socryptic smile—no one can agree on that lady's thoughts, but we do know they were pleasing to her. If you can meet life with this kind of outlook, even if you don't wear Mona Lisa's smile all the time, you will achieve a natural beauty that shines from within, a feeling of tranquility that will see you through any problem you may encounter during your busy, hectic day.

It is with this positive approach that you should consider your makeup selection, keeping in mind that choosing the correct makeup preparations for your skin type is the all-important factor.

Pin back your hair and let's begin.

DAYWEAR PREPARATIONS

If you have PLUS or oily skin, you should never use cream or emollient based preparations, except around the eyes, the upper lip, and the neck, *if*

these areas are dry and unblemished.

NOTE: I cannot caution you too strongly against applying oils and creams to the nose area, an area usually subject to excess oiliness, and to any other oily area. Anyone who advises you otherwise is not knowledgeable in proper skin care.

If you have MINUS or dry skin, you should never use water-and-alcohol based preparations, except on the nose and the areas of the T-zone, *if* these areas are oily.

It is as important to know which preparations are wrong for you as it is to know which you should use.

I have said that the words "foundation" and "base" must be forgotten. Instead we must think of enhancing our skin with a *daywear preparation* that can be used into evening if you are going out. As well as perfecting our skin tone, this preparation is our skin's mantle against the elements— the pollution in the air, the drying effects of sun and wind. The formulas I developed also work to correct your skin's oiliness or to compensate for your skin's dryness, depending on which preparation your skin requires.

APPLYING SKIN PASTE

APPLYING SKIN PASTE

APPLYING COLORED ASTRINGENT

MEDIUMS

Daywear preparations are needed in two basic forms or mediums—an emollient formulation and an astringent based liquid. Because the different areas of your face have different needs, you must have both.

For the PLUS areas: a water-and-alcohol based preparation, tinted closest to your skin color. My preparation for oily skin is called COLORED ASTRINGENT. This lotion continues the corrective treatment of your cleansing routine, acting as a protective agent and a continuous shield against the daily mixture of your skin's oil and the atmosphere's pollutants.

For the BALANCED and MINUS areas: an emollient based preparation, tinted closest to your skin color. My preparation for BALANCED to dry skin is called SKIN PASTE. As it assumes your skin's own texture, it acts as a buffer against wrinkles and as a shield against the damaging effects of exposure. For ease of application, it is applied after a thin veil of my nourishing oil complex, CLEANSING OIL, has been blotted dry.

Not all companies manufacture both mediums in the same shades. You may have to choose different brands if you are not using my preparations. Remember that the color you want might be listed under various commercial names. Take the first preparation with you when you shop for the second to avoid applying two mismatched shades at home.

Remember, too, that the most *effective* products are the ones geared *for your skin type,* not the ones in the prettiest packages or those that list the most promises.

COLOR SELECTION

Choosing a color closest to your natural skin tone is essential for achieving a natural look. However, a slight variation can enhance your complexion:

If your skin tends to look *sallow* and fatigued, with a *yellowish* cast, CHOOSE a daywear preparation with a PINK or HONEY tint. *Avoid* the yellow-toned shades of *beige*.

If your skin tends to look *ruddy* or *reddish* because of diffused capillaries close to the skin surface, CHOOSE a daywear preparation from the BEIGE family. *Avoid* those with a *pink* cast.

If your skin is very *pale* and you wish to give it a warmer color, CHOOSE a daywear preparation that is a shade or two deeper than your natural skin tone. Rouge can be used to add gentle color to your face as well.

APPLICATION

For the PLUS skin: COLORED ASTRINGENT or a water-and-alcohol based daywear preparation. This is to be used on all areas of the PLUS face, except the eye and upper lip areas and the neck, unless blemished.

Follow these steps for a smooth application:

1. Saturate a piece of sterilized cotton with your well-shaken preparation.

2. Apply it to your face, omitting the eye and the upper lip areas and the neck, unless oily.

3. Using a smoothing movement, blot dry with a tissue wrapped around your first two fingers. The color will not be eliminated.

For the eye and the upper lip areas and the neck, if they are MINUS: SKIN PASTE or an emollient based daywear preparation.

Follow these steps for a smooth application:

1. With your index finger, dot a small amount of your preparation under your eyes, on the eyelids, above your upper lip, and on your neck. With your middle finger, smooth the preparation into your skin.

2. Blot these areas with a tissue in this manner: place the tissue against the skin and smooth it with your fingertips. Lift the tissue off. The heat of your fingertips causes any residue to adhere to the tissue, giving you a smoother finish.

NOTE: For persistent dark circles under the eyes, you may use a second application for coverage and protection. If there is still a hint of darkness in the area, use a preparation in a color that is a shade or two lighter than the one used over the rest of your face; this will brighten the area. If your skin has a red or ruddy tone, a preparation with a rosy hue will even your complexion.

For the BALANCED and MINUS skin: SKIN PASTE or an emollient based daywear preparation. This is to be used on all areas of the minus face, except the nose, as it is usually subject to enlarged, clogged pores.

Follow these steps for a smooth application:

1. For easier application of your daywear preparation, saturate a piece of sterilized cotton with a mineral oil complex (CLEANSING OIL) and apply to your face, omitting the nose. Blot thoroughly using a tissue.

2. With your index finger, dot a small amount of your daywear preparation on the right half of your face, starting under the eye (include the eyelid if it is BALANCED to dry), and continue with your cheek area.

3. Using your middle finger, smooth it gently into your skin. Repeat the application on the left side of your face, including the upper lip area, the neck and, lastly, using the smallest amount, the forehead.

4. Blot with a tissue in this manner: place the tissue over the areas and smooth it against your skin with your fingertips. Lift the tissue off. The heat of your fingertips causes any residue to adhere to the tissue, giving you a smoother finish.

When blotting your forehead, extend the tissue over your eyes to blot

the lids. Press the tissue against the inner corners with two fingertips to gently remove any accumulation.

NOTE: For persistent dark circles under the eyes, you may use a second application for coverage and protection. If there is still a hint of darkness in the area, use a preparation in a color that is a shade or two lighter than the one used over the rest of your face; this will brighten the area. If your skin has a red or ruddy tone, a preparation with a rosy hue will even out your complexion.

For the nose area: COLORED ASTRINGENT or a water-and-alcohol based daywear preparation.

Follow these steps for a smooth application:

1. Saturate a piece of sterilized cotton with your well-shaken preparation.

2. Apply it to the entire nose surface.

3. Using a smoothing movement, blot dry with a tissue wrapped around your first two fingers. The color will not be eliminated.

FACE POWDER

NOTE: Those with BALANCED or MINUS skin may use a *cream rouge*. Apply rouge as described in its section below and then follow with the face powder application.

Face powder is still an important part of the whole makeup picture. And it is for everyone, including those very outdoorsy ladies who often refuse to wear it, but should! Powder is perfect for them because it affords the skin added protection against exposure at the same time that it gives the face a pretty look—we all want that.

MEDIUM

There is only one medium for face powder and that is in loose form. Pressed powder is simply not clean enough; in compact form, it is of too heavy a nature to put on your perfect skin. By using and reusing the same puff, you transport oils from your face to the cake, making the powder oily (and using it then could clog a pore and we certainly don't want that).

Loose, non-occlusive or non-pore clogging powder formulated from the finest talc won't cake on your face. This kind of face powder applied from its sifter with a small piece of cotton affords ease of application as well as a finished look.

If a reapplication is needed during the day, carefully handled, a small amount of powder from your sifter will not affect your clothes in the least —a common, unfounded complaint from pressed powder lovers. And there's no reason to want to slap a puff against your soft skin when a quick dab with a small piece of cotton will do.

glow, TRANSLUCENT SUNTAN, for a darker look.

NOTE: A variation in powder color can enhance your skin. A no-color powder can highlight a tanned as well as a pale complexion. A pink shade can heighten a sallow skin, a beige works well on a ruddy one.

COLOR SELECTION

Look for translucent face powder in a shade closest to your natural skin tone. My four most popular shades are TRANSLUCENT, a no-color powder, TRANSLUCENT MIST, a BEIGE color, TRANSLUCENT CAMEO, for a pinkish

APPLICATION

1. Dip a piece of sterilized cotton in your container of loose powder and saturate it heavily.

2. Starting at your jawline, cover your face with a thick amount of powder, working upward, over your eyelids as well. Any powder that adheres to your eyelashes will increase the holding power of your mascara later.

3. Let the powder stay in place for as long as it takes you to brush your eyebrows.

4. Use the cotton to remove all traces of powder. Don't worry about taking off too much; just the right amount will remain on your skin.

★ Stop here to apply a nourishing lip salve, such as my LIP SARTINIZER. Apply it to your bottom lip; it will moisten and prepare your lips for lipstick, our final step.

EYE MAKEUP

Eye shadow can be used very effectively to enhance your eyes, but we must take care not to use too much of a good thing.

MEDIUMS

Eye shadow is available in three popular mediums—cream form, powder-and-applicator, pencils. Each has a limited use.

Shadow in powder form is the most long-lasting and versatile format, appropriate *for all skin types*. It can be applied dry or, as I prefer to use it, applied wet with a slanted brush. This is the proper medium if your eyelids are oily or if they are subject to allergic reactions from cream preparations. The allergy prone should beware of shadows with added iridescence or pearlescence which could cause an irritation. Only pure colors should be used.

Cream-type eye shadow is fine for use on eyelids that tend to be dry. However, creams do not last as long as the powdered shadows and fall into creases more readily. If you have applied your emollient daywear preparation on the eyelids as well as the under-eye area, you do not need the additional emollients in the cream shadow.

Eye shadow pencils present a double problem. The hard leaded ones can pull at the tender skin of the eye area, causing redness at the very least. The softer ones wear away quickly and must be sharpened frequently—the pencil is gone before you can achieve a working point: expensive!

COLOR SELECTION

I want to say only a few words about color because I do not wish to limit your selection in any way. I would like to encourage you to experiment—a much more positive suggestion. I only ask that you choose shadows in the proper medium for your skin type.

I must tell you though that I am often horrified by the shocking look of extreme colors—bright blues and greens especially—circling the eyes. Even women with blue and green eyes should choose soft, subtle pastel or smoky shades rather than glaring crayon-like colors. You want the world to notice YOU, not your eye shadow.

The use of a white or an off-white shadow can present a problem if it is applied noticeably to the brow or upper part of the eyelid. A carefully placed hint of this color, artfully done, can highlight beautifully, but you must practice to avoid an artificial look.

Practice and experiment.

APPLICATION

Where to place shadow is as individual as choosing the right color. Some eyes are complimented by only a thin band of color applied close to the lashes. Those with large eyes might extend the shadow over the lid to the outer corner, moving under the lower lashes.

Small eyes will look larger if the shadow is applied and blended toward the outer half of the upper lid, extended outward and brought under the lower lashes at the outer corner.

For powdered shadow: apply with a slanted, sable-tipped brush. If you are applying it wet, wet the brush and moisten the cake. Stroke the color on gently. Smooth with a fingertip.

For cream shadow: apply the color to your lid with your index finger. Use your middle finger to smooth it in place.

For pencils: use very gentle and careful strokes and blend with a fingertip.

Shadow can be effectively used under your BROW. If the bone protrudes, a shadow a few shades darker than that on the rest of the lid will make it recede. If you need to make the area more prominent, use a lighter color there.

A light touch of rouge well blended just under the outer half of the eyebrow will give you a pretty glow.

Eyebrow Contouring is easily accomplished with the combined use of *a powdered eyebrow cake with brush* and *an eyebrow pencil*, both in the shade closest to your natural coloring.

Using an eyebrow brush, start by brushing the brows again, shaping them to the contour of your eye. If it is sparse, fill in the area with color from the cake. Use the pencil to define the rest of the eyebrow, the descending line after the arch.

I would like to caution you against two errors quite frequently made. The first is bringing the descending line of the brow too close to the eye. Strive for an open-eyed look. And yet—here's the second mistake—do not attempt an exaggerated arch for that always looks artificial and, frequently, bizarre.

Eye Liner must be applied with caution. A thin line at the base of your lashes, both upper and lower, can make the lashes look fuller. The line can also be extended just slightly at the outer corner for a look of mystery. Some eyes can carry a soft, thick line of color, one created with a fatter eyeliner pencil. However, subtlety is the key; too much liner, applied in a Cleopatra-like way, is too obvious.

NOTE: A line of blue applied along the inside of the lower lid will make the whites of your eyes whiter and brighter.

Mascara completes the eye makeup. For easy application, select a wand type mascara; for a fuller lash, a cream or cake-and-brush work well.

Apply mascara to both the top and bottom lashes. You may repeat application several times, going from one eye to the other until you have achieved the desired thickness. Make sure that lashes are full without being matted.

A word on false eyelashes: they are great for very special occasions, those that call for added glamour . . . if you have mastered their application. Choose lashes with a narrow base to avoid a heavy, artificial look— glamorous can easily become garish.

ROUGE

Rouge can create a great variety of looks. It can give your face warmth. It can add color to your cheeks—that interesting look we are all struggling to achieve. Rouge can define or heighten your bone structure.

Experimenting with shades is fine, though I will offer you some suggestions. But I insist that you use the medium suited to your skin type.

MEDIUMS

Those with BALANCED or MINUS skin may choose between a *cream* and a *powdered rouge.*

Those with a PLUS or an ALLERGIC or SENSITIVE skin must use only the dry medium; a cream could block a pore or cause an irritation, depending on your skin type.

I am not in favor of gels or liquids which can coat the skin.

COLOR SELECTION

Choose a rouge that *does not contain* any metallic flecks, pearlescence or iridescence which can cause an irritation on any skin.

A reddish brown rouge works well on almost all complexions.

A light, pale tone skin may be complimented by a pink rouge, never a hard or strong color. Light peach is an attractive choice as well.

For added depth, you might like to combine a brighter red with a second color that has deeper, brown tones, as described below.

APPLICATION

Powdered rouge should be applied with a piece of sterilized cotton. You may use a sable brush if you rinse it after each application. Dust the powder on lightly, never pressing. If you are using cotton, you may turn it over and use the clean side to blend the color carefully.

Cream rouge is applied before face powder for those with BALANCED and MINUS skin only. Apply the preparation with your index finger and smooth it into place with your middle finger. If you wish to reapply rouge later in the day, consider using the powdered type.

Rouge is first applied under the highest point of your cheekbone, then blended over the bone and just beneath. Unfortunately, many of us aren't happy with our cheekbones and apply rouge in all sorts of places, hoping to achieve a bone structure that resembles Katharine Hepburn's. I too was impressed by the natural contour of her face and the lovely planes of her cheeks, but I want to emphasize the word *natural*. She did not achieve her special look by applying obvious makeup. The lesson to be learned from Miss Hepburn is to work with what you have. Or else you might find that you are detracting from your jewel-like eyes by exaggerating your cheekbones to the point of gauntness: it simply won't work.

You can add depth through a slightly intensified color by working with two shades, a brighter, strong red and a reddish brown used to soften it. Apply the red rouge to the cheek area with a wide brush. Apply the browner rouge over the color and around the edges to heighten the area, smoothing and blending with cotton. Check the application in your mirror at various angles to be sure the effect is natural.

NOTE: Any excess of rouge and any line of demarcation can be removed by smoothing with a cotton swab gently applied to the area.

You may also use dry rouge to highlight your temples and the highest point of your browbone. For those who prefer not to use eye shadow on the browbone, a light application of rouge well blended can enhance your face in a very natural way.

LIPSTICK

The beauty of lipstick speaks for itself when it looks luscious on your lips.

In choosing a lipstick, you want one that won't create the suggestion of lines by running into your upper lip area nor one that will dry out your lips and cause them to peel. Lipstick should be a protective agent as well as a beautifier.

Color is your own individual choice, but do consider your clothing before selecting your lipstick if you use very bright colors—a peachy orange would clash with a lavender blouse or dress!

Follow these steps for a smooth and lasting application:

1. Blot off the lip salve you applied earlier, using a tissue.

2. If you have a hard time keeping your lipstick on your lips, dust them lightly with your face powder before applying lipstick.

3. Using a sturdy fine-tipped sable brush, line your lips to improve their shape (this will help hold the lipstick in place, too). You may wish to use a coordinated pencil or even a slightly darker one to better define the lip outline instead.

4. Fill in the outline with lipstick and smooth with your brush.

5. Smooth just a bit of salve (LIP SARTINIZER) on your bottom lip for extra protection and shine.

Always carry a purse-size lip salve with you. Instead of bothering with your lipstick and a mirror when you feel the color fading or the sensation of dryness, you need only discreetly dab a bit of salve on your pinkie and smooth it on your bottom lip.

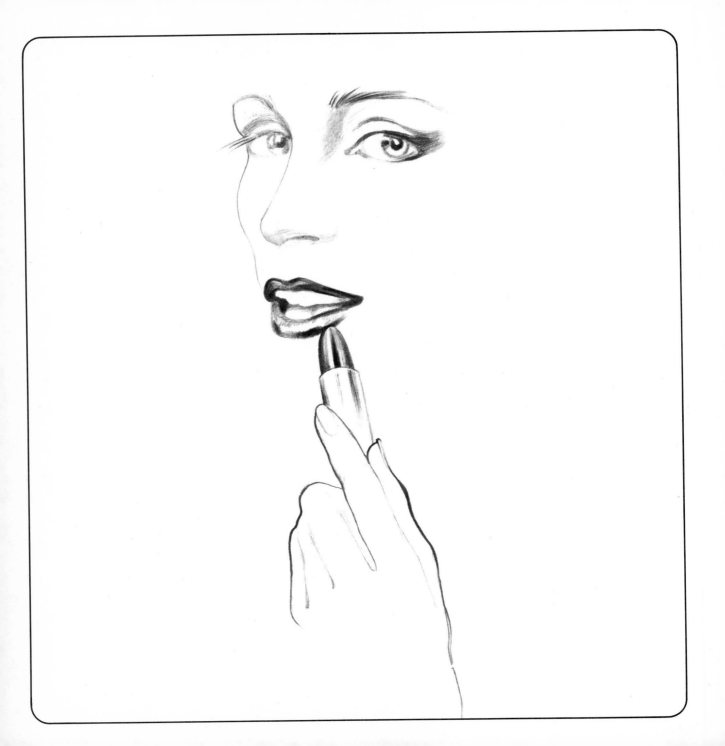

LIGHTING
AND CHECKING

Whether you're making up for day or evening wear, you should always apply your makeup in a well-lighted room—the light above your medicine cabinet is inadequate. You can supplement this with a makeup mirror that has various settings.

The best light is natural sunlight. If you cannot have a makeup area in front of a window, check your makeup in this light with a hand-held mirror.

When applying makeup in the evening, you will have to have sufficient artificial light. If you have a makeup mirror, check the application in both the evening light setting and the fluorescent one—you will be exposed to this last under a theater marquee and the bright neon lights of restaurants and discotheques, as well as in elevators and most public transportation.

For a special evening out, I suggest an intensification of your daytime look: a stronger application of your usual color or perhaps a deeper rouge and shadow. For those who are not sensitive or allergic to pearlescence, you might look for an eye shadow with just a suggestion of this.

Checking your makeup after a careful application is as important as the application itself. Always check your makeup in two different lights. You might need more rouge, perhaps a bit more mascara.

During your makeup application and afterward, be sure to look at your face from all angles. A full-face stance can result in uneven blending and noticeable lines of demarcation.

After checking your makeup in sunlight or at another setting on your makeup mirror, return to the original light you used. For a final scrutiny, hold the mirror at eye level and look at your reflection. If the image you see glows with health and vibrancy, you can unplug your mirror and set forth, knowing that with the little extra time and care you took, you will look delicious all day and evening!

CHECKLIST

**YOUR MAKEUP
ESSENTIALS
PREPARATIONS
AND TOOLS**

Daywear Preparations: a water-and-alcohol based preparation for the PLUS areas; an emollient based preparation for the BALANCED and MINUS areas.

Face Powder: translucent, in loose form.

Eye Shadow in the proper medium; brush for powdered type.

Eyebrow Cake-and-Brush.

Eyebrow Pencil.

Eyebrow Brush: for grooming.

Eye Liner: cake and fine-tipped brush or a soft pencil.

Mascara: cream, cake-and-brush, or wand type.

Rouge: in the proper medium; if desired for powdered rouge, wide brush for general application, smaller brush for detailing.

Lip Salve.

Lipstick with a sable brush for application; a sturdy brush or a pencil for lip-lining.

Sterilized Cotton.

Tissues.

Cotton Swabs.

Makeup Mirror.

5

Problem Skin: Breakthrough or Breakout

Problem skin is not just a teenage dilemma. A congested complexion can plague both the young *and* the mature woman or man. Excess oil produced by your sebaceous glands usually will not disappear with the passing of years. As you reach thirty, forty, fifty, the abundant secretions can further aggravate your skin due to the added stress of our day-to-day living, to our overindulgence in food and drink—our richer tasting of life. An oily skin will certainly not shift into a MINUS category. Nor will there be a radical change in the condition of a sensitive or allergic skin, both of which are con-

sidered "problem" skins, though they are not oily per se.

No matter what your age, if you have a problem skin, be it a +3 or +4, a sensitive or an allergic, or a combination skin, which will also be discussed in this chapter, your main concern and mine is how to cope with and control the condition.

The first step (which you have already taken by reading chapter 2, "Which Skin Type Are You?") is to educate yourself as to your skin's specific characteristics and to then begin the appropriate corrective program. *Using the proper preparations on your skin is paramount.*

THE PLUS SKINS

If you have an oily, aggravated PLUS skin, it is important to understand *why*. Congested pores can be attributed to either a *systemic* problem or a *superficial* problem.

If your skin's oiliness is Systemic, it means that the abundance of oil is a characteristic programmed in your genes or your body's system. It is an inherited condition.

If you are cleansing properly and are still plagued by oily accumulations, blackheads, and enlarged pores, you are probably feeling very confused. You must understand that cleansing alone cannot alter the effects of a glandular imbalance which creates more oily secretions than your pores can handle. The sebaceous glands are feeding more oils into your pores than they can naturally excrete or pass through. You will need to use preparations that can help keep the passages clear by working with your skin to excrete oils more rapidly. My

WHITE ASTRINGENT was especially developed with this goal in mind; it draws impurities to the surface and relieves inflammation.

Superficial problems may result from using the wrong preparations on a complexion that has a tendency to tip toward the PLUS side of the scale.

Using oily substances on your face, such as a moisturizer, will cause you to suffer the pore-blockage problem of a very oily skin. The condition can be quickly remedied by replacing the incorrect preparations with the proper ones. *No oil or emollient based products should ever be used on a PLUS skin.*

Added problems can arise by using excessively caustic substances. These detergent based formulas can strip even an oily skin, drying the scarf cuticle and trapping the excess oils underneath. However, the condition can be corrected by releasing the oils through the use of the proper preparations.

A PLUS skin is often a lazy skin which must be revitalized. The excess oils distend pores, robbing the skin of its elasticity. To correct this, you must follow a treatment program that works to balance the output of oils so that they can be properly distributed over

the skin. Your program must also refine the pores by helping to thin out the heavy, sluggish oils that have become trapped in the passages.

Before you begin a constructive program, you should be able to define the limits of the oily areas of your face. Just as your nose area is almost always oily (for even the MINUS skin), the area around the eyes, the upper lip area, and the neck tend to be dry, even though the rest of your face is PLUS. I say "tend" to be dry because there are no strict rules in nature. In quite a number of cases, these areas can be involved in the clogged pore and blem-

ish condition and would then be treated in the same manner.

Carefully examine these three areas for excess oil, fatty deposits, and sensitivity to determine which products you'll use for morning and evening cleansing and for daywear, astringent or emollient based ones.

NOTE: The area under *the inner corner of the eye* extending downward in an arc may be subject to deposits which lie under the skin surface and appear as tiny, white pinpoints. These accumulations must be drawn to the surface where they can be released.

NOTE: *The sides of the neck* may be subject to blemishes due to a peach-like hair fuzz prevalent here as well as along the jawline. If the sides of your neck are subject to this oily condition, they will be treated with astringent based products. If the center or throat area is clear, you will use emollient based preparations for daywear and cleansing. However, if this area is oily as well, the entire neck will be treated to the PLUS skin program.

NOTE: *The nose,* which is already subject to excess oils, can be especially resistant to correction if the oily secretions adhering to a hair shaft in the follicle harden. These tight, clogged pores can be freed, but be patient; a longer period of correction will be necessary.

As I have said, PLUS skins usually do not lose their oils as you get older. Though a +1 or +2 skin might be able to correct an oily imbalance, this will result from consistent care and not the passing of time. In these cases, the oily condition is *controlled* and the proper care will have to be continued.

The +3 and +4 skins represent a more serious problem because their oily secretions are so excessive that the pores are easily congested, providing the perfect breeding ground for blemishes, pustules, and boils. Often, this is a situation that began at the +2 stage and was allowed to worsen. You can start to correct it now.

THE +3 SKIN

Though problem complexions are often associated with young people, their parents, and grandparents, are not immune. To show you how broad the spectrum is, let me tell you that I have had a six-year-old client and a seventy-year-old client, both suffering with a cystic complaint!

Some teenage problems can be corrected by the time a young woman reaches her twenties, and the reasons for this are not mysterious. A young woman is willing to take more time to understand and care for her skin, more so than her teenage brother or sister. Her tastes change; chocolate shakes and greasy French fries, foods which can aggravate a PLUS skin, are less appealing. She knows that careful attention must be paid to diet.

The reasons for a congested complexion can be more complex than poor eating habits. In some instances, an unblemished teenage complexion can develop hidden problems as the young person matures if, for example, she has begun using makeup products not designed for her skin type. This condition can be corrected by replacing the incorrect preparations with the correct ones. See chapter 4, "Making Makeup Work for You," for specific guidelines. If the problem is systemic, the complaint will stay with you until you master it. Therefore, the mature woman who neglected an earlier breakout may now find herself with the enlarged, clogged pores and blemishes of the +3 skin.

THE +3 SYSTEM

You must keep your skin as clean and as antiseptic as possible. That means following this routine three times a day. Remember that this is an aggravated problem requiring serious dedication to correct it.

In the morning and evening, before dressing:

1. Saturate a piece of sterilized cotton from your roll with astringent (CLEAR ASTRINGENT) and gently cleanse your face, omitting the area around your eyes, the upper lip area, and the neck if these are dry and unblemished.

First cleanse the nose area, then, changing the cotton, move to one cheek, then to the other, and down around your chin. Move to the center of your forehead between the eyebrows and cleanse the area to the right, then the area to the left of the center, including the outer eye area if it is subject to enlarged, clogged pores and blemishes (if not, include this area in step 2).

Use clean cotton as needed, after turning each piece inside out for the maximum four-side usage.

2. If the areas around your eyes, the upper lip area, and the neck are not oily, saturate a clean piece of cotton with a mineral oil complex (CLEANSING OIL) and gently cleanse these areas.

3. Fill your basin or bowl with warm water. Wet your face with clean hands. Lather your face with your wet bar of anti-bacterial, anti-acne soap (1012 SOAP) and make a separate lather in your hands. Work both lathers into your skin using a gentle motion.

4. Holding your elbows out to the sides, rinse your face with the same, soapy water in the basin for a total of *fifteen* times to derive the full treatment benefits of the soap and water aeration.

5. Dry your face with a soft, clean towel.

6. Saturate a clean piece of cotton with well-shaken WHITE ASTRINGENT and apply it to the oily areas of your face, omitting the area around your eyes, the upper lip area, and the neck if these are dry and unblemished. Blot it dry with a tissue.

7. Saturate a clean piece of cotton with a water-and-alcohol based day-wear preparation (COLORED ASTRINGENT) and apply it to the oily areas of your face, omitting the area around your eyes, the upper lip area, and the neck if these are dry and unblemished. Blot it dry with a tissue.

8. Using your index finger, dot a small amount of an emollient daywear preparation (SKIN PASTE) under your eyes, above your upper lip, and on your neck, if these areas are dry and unblemished. Smooth the preparation into your skin with your middle finger. Blot with a tissue.

9. Follow with face powder, eye makeup, powdered rouge, and lipstick as described in chapter 4, "Making Makeup Work for You."

In the evening, before retiring, after you have removed your lipstick and eye makeup as described in chapter 3, "The World's Best (and Simplest) Skin Care System," follow the morning routine through step 5. Continue with:

6. Using one end of a cotton swab, apply my SKIN APPLICATION to your face, omitting the area around your eyes, the upper lip area, and the neck if these are dry and unblemished. Blot it dry with a tissue.

7. Saturate a clean piece of cotton with my well-shaken WHITE ASTRINGENT and apply it to your face, omitting the area around your eyes, the upper lip area, and the neck if these are dry and unblemished. Blot it dry with a tissue.

8. Smooth a small amount of a nourishing cream (SUPERFATTED CREAM) under your eyes, above your upper lip, and on your neck, if these areas are dry and unblemished. Leave it on for ten minutes and then blot it off.

I cannot stress too strongly the importance of my WHITE ASTRINGENT, which soothes problem skin and releases trapped oils at the same time. When the oils are released and the skin is normalized, WHITE ASTRINGENT will maintain the lessened flow of oils.

COLORED ASTRINGENT, the tinted for day and evening-wear version of this preparation, affords around-the-clock healing as it gives your face a beautifully groomed look. No additional product may be used. If more coverage is needed, apply additional applications of COLORED ASTRINGENT, blotting after each application.

SKIN APPLICATION is another of my astringent based products. Its penetrating formulation works extremely well in conjunction with the WHITE ASTRINGENT to heal and prevent blemishes.

MY SPECIAL TREATMENT FOR BLEMISHES

If one or more blemishes appear on your face, incorporate the use of SKIN APPLICATION in your morning routine in this manner:

Follow the morning program through step 5. Continue with:

6. With one end of a cotton swab that has been saturated with SKIN APPLICATION, dot each blemish. Blot dry with a tissue.

7. Saturate a clean piece of cotton with well-shaken WHITE ASTRINGENT and apply it to your face, omitting the area around your eyes, the upper lip area, and the neck if dry and unblemished. Blot it dry with a tissue.

8. Saturate a clean piece of cotton with a water-and-alcohol based daywear preparation (COLORED ASTRINGENT) and apply it to your face, omitting the area around your eyes, the upper lip area, and the neck if these are dry and unblemished. Blot it dry with a tissue.

9. If the blemish(es) is (are) still red and noticeable, additionally dot each with one end of a cotton swab that has been saturated with well-shaken WHITE ASTRINGENT. Wait a few seconds and then blot the outer edges and lightly on the center. This will heal as well as conceal the blemish.

10. Using your index finger, dot a small amount of an emollient based daywear preparation (SKIN PASTE) under your eyes, above your upper lip, and on your neck, if these areas are dry and unblemished. Smooth the preparation into your skin with your middle finger. Blot with a tissue.

11. Follow with face powder, eye makeup, powdered rouge, and lipstick as described in chapter 4, "Making Makeup Work for You."

NOTE: SKIN APPLICATION + WHITE ASTRINGENT can be used to stop a blemish before it appears. Incorporate SKIN APPLICATION in your morning/evening routine as soon as you *feel* the first symptom of an oncoming blemish, the soreness beneath the skin surface. Apply as explained above, and follow with WHITE ASTRINGENT and the other steps. The blemish will dissipate before it has a chance to erupt.

SKIN APPLICATION + WHITE ASTRINGENT is helpful when you feel a blemish developing on an area you cannot reach directly, such as the inner membrane of a nostril. My two preparations can heal the most uncomfortable irritations quickly by penetrating from the outside surface.

Though I have said that problem skin can occur at any age, I am sure you are wondering why it begins primarily during the teenage years, complicating your already changing lifestyle. It is because your body is going through its most important changes, too.

Girls often associate a blemished complexion with the arrival of their first menstrual cycle, at the age of twelve or thirteen, in most cases. Your complexion will readily show the changes going on inside you.

Once a steady monthly pattern is established, any variation, such as a late period, might show a reaction on your complexion because your body will be retaining certain fluids and toxic poisons it should have released. Following the correct skin care program can strengthen your skin, making it immune to such reactions.

Young women can experience a breakout due to facial hair, that soft peach-like fuzz especially prevalent around the jawline and sides of the face. If your excess secretions are oily or fluid enough, they may pass easily through the pores. However, if they cornify, or harden, rapidly, they will cling to the hair shaft, clogging the pore. If an inflammation develops, you must understand that this does not necessarily point to an allergic reaction. The inflammation and pus are nature's softening agents which help the clog pass through to the surface. SKIN APPLICATION + WHITE ASTRINGENT are exceptionally helpful in treating and preventing this skin eruption.

Young men will frequently notice a complexion change when they begin to mature as well. Further complication occurs with the first signs of hair growth, along the lower cheeks and the jawline, at the age of fifteen or sixteen. The sprouting of hairs, however anticipated, can irritate the pores as oily secretions cling to the shaft, blocking the passage and trapping the oils under the surface.

The necessity of shaving can worsen the problem as blemishes can interfere and get knicked. Ingrown hairs present another form of irritation. Follow these steps every morning for the smoothest, least irritating shave:

1. Saturate a clean piece of cotton with astringent (CLEAR ASTRINGENT) and gently cleanse your face.

2. Fill your basin or bowl with warm water. Wet both your face and your bar of anti-bacterial, anti-acne soap (1012 SOAP). Lather your face with the soap and then make a separate lather in your clean hands. With your fingers, work both lathers into your skin.

3. Holding your elbows out to the sides, rinse your face with the same, soapy water in the basin for a total of *fifteen* times to derive the full treatment benefits of the soap. Blot your face lightly with a soft, clean towel.

4. Apply a shaving lather to your beard and let it soften the hairs for three to five minutes before you begin to shave.

5. Shave with careful strokes, avoiding knicking blemishes as much as you can.

6. After you have rinsed all traces of lather from your face, apply well-shaken WHITE ASTRINGENT to each of the blemishes. Blot dry for invisible healing. Use well-shaken WHITE ASTRINGENT on your neck as well if you have any redness from shaving irritation or ingrown hairs. My preparation will heal the infection and strengthen the skin, enabling it to fight future irritations.

THE WHITE ASTRINGENT COMPRESS FOR +3 AND +4 SKIN

If your blemishes become more intensified or if your skin is exceedingly oily, my WHITE ASTRINGENT should be used as a compress over the entire area. Follow these steps once a day, in addition to your three-times-a-day program:

1. After following your morning routine through step 5, using one end of a cotton swab, apply SKIN APPLICATION to the blemished or excessively oily areas of your face, omitting the area around your eyes, the upper lip area, and the neck if these are dry and unblemished. Blot it dry with a tissue.

2. Saturate thin layers of cotton with your well-shaken WHITE ASTRINGENT, taking pieces of cotton that are just slightly smaller than the area you want to cover. (You will find that the roll of sterilized cotton separates easily into layers, like a multiple-ply tissue.)

3. Stretch the cotton over the problem areas, using as many different pieces as needed. You will find it easier to use one piece for each cheek, one for the chin area, one for the forehead, one for the nose, always making each just short of the size needed so that it can be stretched tightly.

4. Leave the cotton compress(es) in place until dry, about *fifteen* minutes. Peel off and discard.

Depend on this treatment to clear blemishes—squeezing them won't effectively clear pores and can do harm. I have found that by holding the WHITE ASTRINGENT against the skin through the use of cotton, the benefits of this preparation are greatly increased. Once the blemishes are gone, you may use the WHITE ASTRINGENT compress twice a week to control your skin's oiliness.

When is a good time to do the compress? Any time that is convenient for you. For example, a student can do it while studying. You might like to use it before going out in the evening or after you've come home, before retiring.

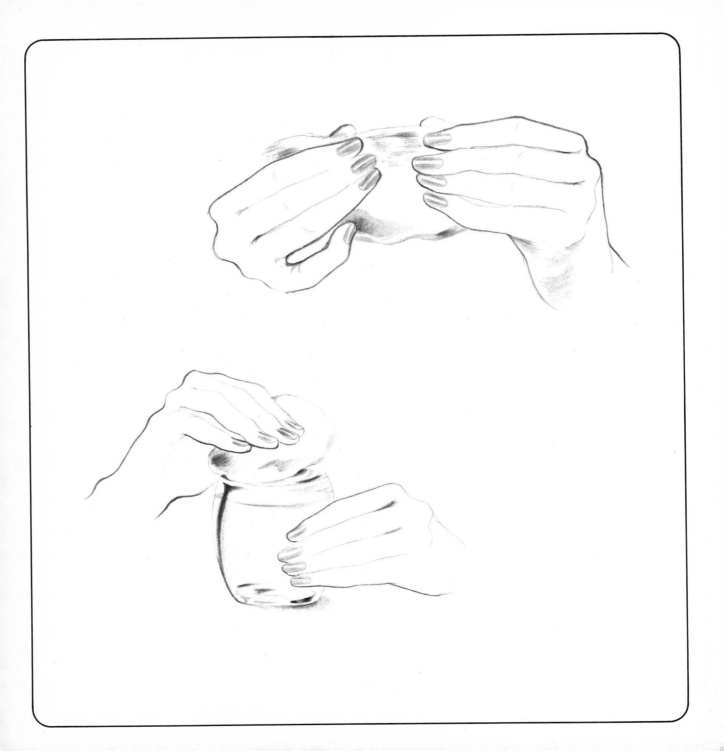

If you prefer applying the compress before retiring, follow your nighttime cleansing directions through step 6, the use of SKIN APPLICATION. Follow step 7, the application of WHITE ASTRINGENT, with the WHITE ASTRINGENT compress described above.

When dry, remove the cotton which, when rolled into a ball, can be used to gently remove some of the WHITE ASTRINGENT residue. Now you can proceed to step 8, the application of a nourishing cream (for the area around the eyes, the upper lip area, and the neck only if these are dry and unblemished).

THE +4 SKIN

Early care started after the first sign of trouble can prevent future complications. But what if you are already plagued by them? Let's start by examining exactly what skin problems characterize this condition.

A PUSTULE is a blemish that can become infected with pus, both at the skin surface and beneath. It has a strong tendency to erupt, easing painful pressure.

A BOIL is a blind inflammation. The area is reddened and sore, with no obvious channel for escape.

A CYST is a very deep accumulation of sebaceous material under the skin surface; it feels like a hard lump. The accumulation is far greater than a fatty deposit.

These are the three most frequent problems that signal the +4 skin. This complexion requires very careful, very thorough care because it cannot clear itself by itself, nor will it go away with wishful thinking.

I want to *alert* you because you cannot allow your skin to go without the necessary treatment and I want to *encourage* you because you are always able to help yourself.

THE +4 SYSTEM

This program must be followed for a minimum of three times a day, four if possible. In the morning, midday, and evening, before dressing:

1. Saturate a piece of sterilized cotton from your roll with astringent (CLEAR ASTRINGENT) and gently cleanse your face, omitting the area around your eyes, the upper lip area, and the neck unless these areas are subject to enlarged, clogged pores and blemishes.

First cleanse the nose area, then, changing cotton, move to one cheek, then to the other, and down around your chin. Move to the center of your forehead between the eyebrows and cleanse the area to the right and then the area to the left of the center, including the outer eye area to the hairline if it is subject to enlarged, clogged pores and blemishes (if not, include this area in step 2).

Use clean cotton as needed after turning each piece inside out for the maximum four-side usage.

2. If the area around your eyes, the upper lip area, and the neck are not oily, saturate a clean piece of cotton with a mineral oil complex (CLEANSING OIL) and gently cleanse these areas.

3. Fill your basin or bowl with warm water. Wet your face with clean hands. Lather your face with your wet bar of anti-bacterial, anti-acne soap (1012 SOAP) and make a separate lather in your hands. Work both lathers into your skin using a gentle motion.

4. Holding your elbows out to the sides, rinse your face with the same soapy water in the basin for a total of *fifteen* times to derive the full treatment benefits of the soap.

5. Dry your face with a soft, clean towel.

6. Using one end of a cotton swab, apply SKIN APPLICATION to your face, omitting the area around your eyes, the upper lip area, and the neck unless these areas are subject to enlarged, clogged pores and blemishes. Blot it dry with a tissue.

7. Saturate a clean piece of cotton with well-shaken WHITE ASTRINGENT and apply it to your face, omitting the area around your eyes, the upper lip area, and the neck unless these areas are subject to enlarged, clogged pores and blemishes. Blot it dry with a tissue.

8. Saturate a clean piece of cotton with a water-and-alcohol based daywear preparation (COLORED ASTRINGENT) and apply it to your face, omitting the area around your eyes, the upper lip area, and the neck unless these areas are subject to enlarged, clogged pores and blemishes. A second and third application may be blended in if more coverage is desired.

9. If the blemishes are still noticeable, use one end of a cotton swab to dot each with well-shaken WHITE ASTRINGENT. Blot the edges and the center lightly for invisible healing.

10. Using your index finger, dot a small amount of an emollient daywear preparation (SKIN PASTE) under your eyes, above your upper lip, and on your neck if these are not oily. Smooth the preparation into your skin with your middle finger. Blot with a tissue.

11. Follow with face powder, eye makeup, powdered rouge, and lipstick as described in chapter 4, "Making Makeup Work for You."

In the evening, before retiring, after you have removed your lipstick and eye makeup as described in chapter 3, "The World's Best (and Simplest) Skin Care System," follow the morning routine through steps 6 and 7, the use of SKIN APPLICATION and WHITE ASTRINGENT. Continue with:

7. The WHITE ASTRINGENT compress as described in the above section. Leave the compress(es) on for a full *fifteen* minutes to let your skin fully absorb the preparation's healing properties.

8. After removing the compress(es), smooth a small amount of a nourishing cream (SUPERFATTED CREAM) under your eyes, above your upper lip, and on your neck, if these areas are not oily. Leave it on for ten minutes and then blot it off.

I know that, whether you have one blemish or many, there is always the temptation to squeeze. I can give you not only one, but three good reasons for resisting this powerful urge.

First of all, the chances are that you will not be able to remove all the sebaceous material. Embedments that have hardened become very resistant. In trying to push them out of the pore, you may break the outer layer of skin, leave a residue subsurface, creating scars and, possibly, pitting—my second good reason. Scar tissue can never be restored.

Thirdly, in squeezing out the sebaceous pus and the blackhead, you leave the pore stretched, creating a bigger area to trap future oils.

The next time you look into the mirror with eager fingertips, reach for SKIN APPLICATION + WHITE ASTRINGENT and let their combined efforts dissolve the offender for you.

Try to keep your hands away from your face at all times. Avoid the nervous habit of brushing the face with your fingers. Try not to rest your cheek in the palm of your hand— hands, even when clean, have active sweat glands in the fingertips that can add to surface soil on your skin. If you must touch, use the back of your fingers.

No matter how troubled you feel about your complexion, let me say that it is never a good idea to hide behind a heavy covering of makeup, certainly not when a water-and-alcohol based preparation can be formulated well enough to conceal without worsening the condition of your skin. Heavy creams and "cover-up" products can only aggravate skin by further clogging your pores.

When should you consult a dermatologist? When you find that the acne is very severe or cystic and that your skin keeps reinfecting itself. A dermatologist can prescribe an antibiotic to supplement your external care to help clear the infection.

NOTE: Before you begin taking an antibiotic, you may wish to consult with your dermatologist about the possible side effects.

However, I do not suggest that you follow all of a dermatologist's or any physician's advice blindly. Dermatological practices such as dermabrasion and chemosurgery can harm by forcing the skin to shed layers, a traumatic reaction it is not always prepared to cope with, especially if the acne condition is still prevalent, with the possibility of returning. You need to follow a program that will work to open pores and release trapped oils, not one that will strip or exfoliate the surface skin, sensitizing it. Consistent care with the proper preparations will give you far better and more lasting results than any drastic, harsh measures. I will discuss the proper times to undertake these procedures in chapter 11, "Cosmetic Surgery: Promiscuous or Prescribed?"

I'm sure that you want to know how long you will have to wait before seeing results. Impatience is normal, as we are all eager to have beautiful glowing skin.

If you are using the correct preparations as often as I have advised, you may see results in a matter of weeks. Since the main objective of this program is to expel the sluggish oils that are trapped in the pores, you may notice a transition period during which the skin seems more oily than before. This excessive but necessary oily secretion will correct itself in a few weeks' time—a few months for the more aggravated complexions, remembering that this can vary depending on individual circumstances.

If the problem is superficial—a tem- porary reaction to a certain food or cosmetic product—your skin may gain a clear and pretty luster right away. But if the problem is systemic, related to an upset in your glandular functioning, then patience and more frequent attention will be needed.

Your improvement rate will depend on the texture of your skin as well as the seriousness of the problem. A thin, rose petal type skin will rid itself of oils at a faster rate than the thicker, gardenia petal type skin. With the former, there is less distance for the oils to travel to the surface, less time in which to harden in the pores.

Excess oils will pass more readily through a skin that is elastic than through a skin that is sluggish. Just as children learn to walk or talk at different ages, so do certain skins respond more quickly or slowly than others.

You may notice that, as you care for your skin, one area of your face breaks out just as another has healed. Often you must strengthen your complexion, area by area, until the last holdout is won over.

The atmosphere and the foods we eat are two other factors that can influence our progress—both will be discussed in later chapters.

Many women ask if it is true that English women have marvelous skin. Not always. An alabaster complexion is superb in any country, but if the Englishwoman has a problem skin, it can be as badly affected as any other.

Black skin can have a greater luster than other skins. But it is achieved through no less effort. In working with women who have black skin, I have found that it takes a little more time, in fact, to correct an excess oiliness. It must be handled more delicately as well; black skin is more prone to pigment changes than a white skin—the result of the pressure of embedments.

Once your skin shows very clear signs of improvement, you can begin a maintenance program. When your blemishes are cleared, when you stop breaking out or your skin is no longer excessively oily, you may gradually stop using SKIN APPLICATION. A corrected +4 skin can go on a +3 program.

When the pore passages are clearing rapidly, when there are fewer blackheads and blemishes, a +3 can start a +2 program, always returning to the use of WHITE ASTRINGENT, and SKIN APPLICATION, if needed. You can control a PLUS skin and have a clear, lustrous complexion.

THE COMBINATION SKIN

When I use the term COMBINATION skin, I am referring to a skin which is fundamentally a PLUS or oily skin but which now, because of exposure and possibly the use of the incorrect preparations, feels dry.

The most important thing to remember is that your skin is still an oily skin. It has been damaged and therefore feels as though it has been "dried out," but this is definitely not the case. The excess oils are still present in the form of fatty accumulations that feel and look like bumps under the skin surface. The oil has not disappeared; it is trapped and cannot break through the parched layer to the surface.

How has the top layer of skin become dry? Most often it is due to overexposure to the sun and a lack of sufficient protection against the other elements. By not taking the necessary precautions, you have enabled the sun to parch the scarf cuticle or top layer of skin, leaving it taut and uncomfortable. It looks dry, it feels dry, but *it is not a dry skin and should not be treated with preparations reserved for a dry skin.* Treating your complexion with emollient based preparations alone would further aggravate your skin by further blocking the pores. Treating your complexion with astringent based preparations alone would further dry the top layer of skin. What then is the answer?

We must seek a middle road, combining the best of the two divergent cleansing/treatment systems to ease the skin back to its natural state, which would be toward PLUS. Cleansing will be done with an emollient preparation. The daywear preparations for both the PLUS and the MINUS skins will be used in conjunction. This combination system will help soften the scarf cuticle without blocking the overloaded pores.

The areas of your face that tend to be dry and usually unblemished—the area around your eyes, the upper lip area, and the neck—will be treated on the MINUS skin program solely. The nose area which secretes more oil than the rest of your face, in most cases, and which has probably withstood the drying effect of the sun, will be treated on the PLUS program solely. Of course, there are exceptions to both these situations, in which case the areas should be treated accordingly.

THE COMBINATION SYSTEM

In the morning and optionally in the evening, before dressing:

1. Saturate a clean piece of sterilized cotton from your roll with a mineral oil complex (CLEANSING OIL) and gently cleanse your face, omitting your nose and any other areas subject to excess oiliness, such as those comprising the T-zone.

Cleanse the right side of your face first, using a sweeping movement from the inner corner of the eye extending outward over the cheek and jaw area. Use the reverse side of the cotton and then turn it inside out for the maximum four-side usage. Repeat this for the left side of your face. Move to the center of your forehead and cleanse to the right, then to the left of the center. With clean cotton, go across the chin. Cleanse the neck from the center to the right, the center to the left.

Use clean cotton as needed until all soil is removed. Do not blot.

2. Saturate a clean piece of cotton with astringent (CLEAR ASTRINGENT) and cleanse the nose, being sure to clean in the curve of the nostrils and beneath the tip. If the scarf cuticle of the T-zone (the forehead, nose, and chin) or any area thereof is not parched, if it exudes oil or develops a noticeable shine during the day, cleanse with astringent rather than oil.

3. Fill your basin or bowl with warm water. Wet your face with clean hands. Lather your face with your wet bar of fatty acid based soap (SUPER-FATTED SOAP) and then make a separate lather in your hands. Work both lathers into your skin using a gentle motion. The soap combines with the oil residue to create an emulsion which softens your skin.

4. Holding your elbows out to the sides, rinse your face with the water in the basin for a total of *fifteen* times to derive the full treatment benefits of the emulsion.

5. Dry your face with a soft, clean towel.

6. Saturate a clean piece of cotton with a water-and-alcohol based daywear preparation (COLORED ASTRINGENT) and apply it to your face, omitting the area around your eyes, the upper lip area, and the neck if these are normally dry and unblemished. Blot dry with a tissue. This preparation helps the skin eliminate its excess oils.

7. Using your index finger, dot a small amount of an emollient daywear preparation (SKIN PASTE) on your face, omitting the nose and any other areas subject to excess oiliness, such as those comprising the T-zone.

First apply the preparation on the right half of your face, starting under the eye. Continue to your cheek area, using your middle finger to gently smooth it into your skin. Repeat the application to the other side of your face, including the upper lip area and the neck. Include the chin and forehead only if the scarf cuticle is parched. Blot with a tissue. This preparation keeps the skin pliant during the day to prevent wrinkling.

8. Follow with face powder, eye makeup, powdered rouge, and lipstick as described in chapter 4, "Making Makeup Work for You."

In the evening, before retiring, after you have removed your lipstick and eye makeup as described in chapter 3, "The World's Best (and Simplest) Skin Care System," follow the morning routine through step 5. Continue with:

6. Smooth a light nourishing cream (SUPERFATTED CREAM) on your face and neck, omitting the nose and any other areas subject to excess oiliness, such as those comprising the T-zone. Leave it on for *ten* minutes. Gently blot it off.

NOTE: If the area around your eyes, the upper lip area, and the neck are very dry, you may use a collagen (protein) cream (HEAVY NIGHT CREAM). Leave it on these areas for *fifteen* minutes and gently blot it off.

7. Saturate a clean piece of cotton with well-shaken WHITE ASTRINGENT and use it to remove the cream, omitting the area around your eyes, the upper lip area, and the neck if these are normally dry and unblemished. Blot it dry with a tissue.

With consistent care, your complexion will improve each day. When your skin has softened, due to the release of trapped oils, you may change to a mildly corrective program, such as the +2 program to correct the natural oiliness of your PLUS complexion. If you find that your skin's oiliness is excessive, switch to the +3 system combining my WHITE ASTRINGENT and SKIN APPLICATION.

You will additionally follow the guidelines set forth in chapter 10, "Take Care," before you expose yourself to the sun again. The proper precautions as well as the proper preparations are needed to prevent this problem from recurring.

The SENSITIVE and the ALLERGIC skins are often confused because both react to generally the same things—the use of a certain cosmetic, the ingestion of a certain drug or food. However, there are great differences between these two skin types and I will discuss them separately.

THE SENSITIVE SKIN

A sensitive skin is a skin that reacts to stress as well as some foods or medications and develops an irritation or reddish blotch. Because it is generally not a PLUS skin, it is not subject to deposits or blackheads. It won't be secreting enough oil to be placed on a totally corrective program; however, the properties in my WHITE ASTRINGENT can strengthen the skin, making it resistant to future outbreaks. The SENSITIVE skin can most benefit from a combination program.

THE SENSITIVE SKIN SYSTEM

In the morning and optionally in the evening, before dressing:

1. Saturate a clean piece of sterilized cotton from your roll with a mineral oil complex (CLEANSING OIL) and gently cleanse your face, omitting your nose, as it is usually subject to enlarged, clogged pores.

Cleanse the right side of your face first, using a sweeping movement from the inner corner of your eye extending outward over the cheek and jaw area. Use the reverse side of the cotton and then turn it inside out for the maximum four-side usage. Repeat this for the left side of your face. Move to the center of your forehead and cleanse to the right, then to the left of the center. With clean cotton, go across the chin. Cleanse the neck, if unblemished, from the center to the right, the center to the left.

Use clean cotton as needed until all soil is removed. Do not blot.

2. Saturate a clean piece of cotton with astringent (CLEAR ASTRINGENT) and cleanse the nose as it is usually subject to enlarged, clogged pores. Be sure to clean in the curve of the nostrils and beneath the tip.

3. Fill your basin or bowl with warm water. Wet your face with clean hands. Lather your face with your wet bar of fatty acid based soap (SUPERFATTED SOAP) and then make a separate lather in your hands. Work both lathers into your skin using a gentle motion.

4. Holding your elbows out to the sides, rinse your face with the water in the basin for a total of *fifteen* times to derive the full treatment benefits of the oil and soap emulsion.

5. Dry your face with a soft, clean towel.

6. Saturate a clean piece of cotton with a water-and-alcohol based daywear preparation (COLORED ASTRINGENT) and apply it to your face, omitting the area around your eyes, the upper lip area, and the neck if these are dry. Blot dry with a tissue.

7. Using your index finger, dot a small amount of an emollient daywear preparation (SKIN PASTE) on your face, omitting your nose, as it is usually subject to enlarged, clogged pores.

First apply the preparation on the right half of your face, starting under the eye. Continue to your cheek area, using your middle finger to gently smooth it into your skin. Repeat the application to the left side of your face, including the upper lip area, the chin and neck, and lastly, using the least amount, the forehead. Blot with a tissue.

8. Using one end of a cotton swab, apply my well-shaken WHITE ASTRINGENT to any blotch or irritation. Wait for a few seconds and blot the edges and the center lightly with the other end of the swab for invisible healing.

NOTE: My WHITE ASTRINGENT and COLORED ASTRINGENT draw impurities to the surface and relieve inflammation while the SKIN PASTE keeps skin supple.

9. Follow with face powder, eye makeup, rouge, and lipstick as described in chapter 4, "Making Makeup Work for You."

In the evening, before retiring, after you have removed your lipstick and eye makeup as described in chapter 3, "The World's Best (and Simplest) Skin Care System," follow the morning routine through step 5. Continue with:

6. Smooth a light nourishing cream (SUPERFATTED CREAM) on your face and neck, omitting the nose, as it is usually subject to enlarged, clogged pores. Leave it on for *ten* minutes and then gently blot it off.

7. Saturate a clean piece of cotton with well-shaken WHITE ASTRINGENT and use it to remove the cream, omitting the area around your eyes, the upper lip area, and the neck if these are dry. Blot it dry with a tissue. Using one end of a cotton swab, apply an additional dab to any irritation.

Once your skin is strengthened, it won't react as readily to foods or medications or stress. Your body will find channels other than the pores of your face through which it can eliminate the substances that caused the irritation. Once your skin no longer shows

this sensitivity, it can be treated with the totally emollient program for BALANCED skin.

THE TEA BAG TREATMENT FOR SENSITIVE AND ALLERGIC SKINS

Though the sensitive and the allergic are two distinct skin types, both react to many of the same things and both respond to the soothing *Tea Bag Treatment,* a treat for your skin.

Tea contains tannic acid, a healing agent. Buy the least expensive brand at your supermarket—the cheaper the tea, the more tannic acid it contains. After following your morning or evening routine through step 5, continue with this procedure daily during breakouts:

1. Pour approximately one cup of just boiled water into a small receptacle.

2. Steep two tea bags in the water and leave them to cool.

3. When the solution is room temperature, about five or ten minutes later, holding both tea bags together, dip them into the liquid and apply to your face.

4. Repeat this application for five minutes, always dipping the bags in the tea and dabbing them on your skin. Blot dry.

5. Discard the tea and the bags.

THE ALLERGIC SKIN

The ALLERGIC skin reflects a more complex problem than the sensitive skin. It is a characteristic you must learn to accept because, like an oily skin, it will not disappear, though on occasion you might outgrow your allergy. The ALLERGIC skin must be kept under constant control and requires a consistent program.

In addition to avoiding those foods which you know from past experience will cause an outbreak of hives or other irritation, you must pay careful attention to which preparations you apply to your face. The ALLERGIC complexion reacts, generally, to emollient based products—creams are not for you! The properties in my WHITE ASTRINGENT can help strengthen your skin as well as draw out the impurities, subdue the inflammation, and clear the skin.

Because we don't want to overly dry the skin, the ALLERGIC skin will be treated to the mildly corrective +1 program. However, if this treatment creates a feeling of dryness, you can place your complexion on the *Combination* program described earlier in this chapter—this will control the allergic reaction and the dryness at the same time.

THE +1 SYSTEM FOR ALLERGIC SKIN

In the morning and optionally in the evening, before dressing:

1. Saturate a clean piece of sterilized cotton from your roll with astringent (CLEAR ASTRINGENT) and gently cleanse your face, omitting the area around your eyes, the upper lip area, and the neck, if these are dry.

First cleanse the nose area, then move to one cheek, then to the other and down around your chin. Use the reverse side of the cotton and then turn it inside out for the maximum four-side usage. Move to the center of your forehead between the eyebrows and first cleanse the area to the right, then the left, including the outer eye area to the hairline if it is subject to allergic reactions (if not, include this area in step 2).

Use fresh cotton until it stays clean.

2. Saturate a clean piece of cotton with a mineral oil complex (CLEANSING OIL) and cleanse the area around your eyes, the upper lip area, and the neck if these areas are dry and not subject to enlarged, clogged pores and blemishes.

NOTE: If your eyelids are involved in the allergic condition, omit cleansing with any oil.

3. Fill your basin or bowl with warm water. Wet your face with clean hands. Lather your face with your wet anti-bacterial, anti-acne soap (1012 SOAP) and then make a separate lather in your hands. Gently work both lathers into your skin.

4. Holding your elbows out to the sides, rinse your face with the water in the basin for a total of *fifteen* times to derive the full treatment benefits of the soap.

5. Dry your face with a soft, clean towel.

6. Saturate a clean piece of cotton with a water-and-alcohol based day-wear preparation (COLORED ASTRINGENT) and apply it to your face, omitting the area around your eyes, the upper lip area, and the neck if these areas are dry and unblemished.

7. Using your index finger, dot a small amount of an emollient daywear preparation (SKIN PASTE) under your eyes, above your upper lip, and on your neck, if these areas are dry and unblemished. Smooth the preparation into your skin with your middle finger. Blot with a tissue.

NOTE: If your eyelids suffer from allergic reactions, omit using any makeup on these areas. Apply my well-shaken WHITE ASTRINGENT to the irritation(s) and blot. Repeat this before retiring. If the allergy persists, check with your dermatologist.

8. Follow with face powder, allowed eye makeup, powdered rouge (no iridescence!), and lipstick as described in chapter 4, "Making Makeup Work for You."

In the evening, before retiring, after removing your lipstick and eye makeup as described in chapter 3, "The World's Best (and Simplest) Skin Care System," follow the morning routine through step 5. Continue with:

6. Saturate a clean piece of cotton with my well-shaken WHITE ASTRINGENT and apply it to your face, omitting the area around the eyes, the upper lip area, and the neck if these areas are dry and unblemished; blot dry with tissue. Apply to your eyelids if involved in allergic reaction; blot.

7. Smooth a light nourishing cream (SUPERFATTED CREAM) under the eyes, above the upper lip, and on the neck, if these areas are dry and unblemished. Leave it on for *ten* minutes and then blot it off.

In addition to your at-home routines, you may wish to consult with your physician about antibiotics which might help both your skin and your body fight off the allergic reactions. Watching your diet is equally important, a subject I will discuss in chapter 9, "Skin Nutrition."

6

Your Future Face

. . . FOR THE YOUNG COMPLEXION

I want you to to be able to face the future with a radiant complexion. That means learning to care for your skin today.

Everyone is born with good skin, but only a small percentage are fortunate enough to maintain this. The rest of us have to be concerned with the changes that can occur.

Those with BALANCED to MINUS skin will have to be careful as they reach the age of eighteen, an important milestone. Until then, your cells are able to renew themselves rapidly, compensating for overexposure to the sun and the elements such as the cold and the wind. But once you turn eighteen, these natural processes of skin rejuvenation begin to slow down and you may see the first signs of a wrinkle. Those with a pre-tendency toward PLUS or oily skin may notice acne manifestations as early as the age of twelve or thirteen, at the onset of puberty or, in some cases, even earlier.

Recognizing your skin's characteristics at a young age will help you prevent an aggravation of these problems in the years to come.

THE PLUS SKIN:
A PROBLEM OF OILINESS

Young skins often have problems with oily secretions. Oil which, in a balanced complexion, is secreted to keep your skin soft and supple is, in these cases, produced in excess. Your glands are working overtime, forming more oil than your skin can cope with. Your skin can become lazy and sluggish. If this happens, oils get trapped in pores and harden, clogging the passage and the opening.

If you notice excess oiliness on your face, on its own or with the additional complication of blackheads and blemishes, you will realize that your skin falls into a PLUS category.

The first step toward correcting this oiliness is in cleansing, with an astringent, followed with a special soap and water treatment. You will want to read chapter 3, "The World's Best (and Simplest) Skin Care System," if the condition is mild; chapter 5, "Problem Skin: Breakthrough or Breakout," if it is more severe. Remember that you must choose your preparations carefully. You don't want to use anything that contains oil or is oil based. This means you mustn't use any kind of moisturizer or cream on the oily areas. Products that come in the form of gels are to be avoided as well as other preparations in tube form—out of necessity, these are formulated with ingredients that shouldn't come in contact with a PLUS skin.

Diet is a contributor to the quality of your skin and requires careful thought. There have been many conflicting reports concerning which foods are or are not harmful to your complexion. I have found, during my many years of working with problem skins, that, as a general rule, you will get an adverse reaction from certain foods if you have an oily skin that is subject to clogged pores.

Greasy, fried foods, rich foods such as starches and desserts, chocolate and shellfish are the worst culprits. I suggest that you follow my suggested diet outlined in chapter 9, "Skin Nutrition."

PLUS skin is usually inherited and, in some cases, can be aggravated by certain products used on your skin—a cream will clog pores and worsen a slightly oily complexion.

An oily complexion given to breaking out does not, as a rule, correct itself when you reach a specific age.

Oily skin that is uncared for more frequently persists and becomes further complicated. You are fortunate that you can correct the problem now and stop it from recurring.

THE MINUS SKIN:
A PROBLEM OF DRYNESS

Skins that appear to be balanced and healthy while you're still in your teens can hide a problem of dryness that, in the future, will age your skin prematurely. Good bone structure and resiliency on the part of your skin might forestall this, but only proper care will keep your complexion looking young.

It is never too early to give serious thought to starting a constructive program. Though the signs of a MINUS skin—an uncomfortable feeling after washing and chapping after exposure—can begin at any age, the attention you give your face now can delay this.

You must cleanse with oil, not a cream which can cause you to rub makeup and soil into your skin before it is wiped off. Cream will be used as a nourishing treatment after your face has been cleansed with oil and treated to a special soap and water bath. See my chapter 3, "The World's Best (and Simplest) Skin Care System," for specific guidelines to caring for your face.

Learn about the different factors that cause your skin to show age. Your worst adversary is the sun. You have to realize the hazards of basking in the sunshine for long periods of time. In chapter 10, you will find specific guidelines for your skin type. You needn't wrap yourself up like a mummy, but take care that you don't wrinkle like a prune!

What exactly does the sun do to your skin? It causes the surface oils to dry up at a rapid rate, making your face feel taut. You need this precious oil to keep your face from wrinkling —the oil softens the skin and helps prevent expression lines from forming.

Expression lines are another aging factor. You can't stop yourself from showing emotion—though you should try to curb your grimacing—and to compensate you need added protection all through the day. You'll be glad to hear that this can come, in part, from the makeup you've been hoping to wear, but it will have to be the right kind of makeup (more about that soon).

UNDER EYES

UPPER LIP

NECK

Although you want to nourish your MINUS skin, you don't want to use preparations that will lie heavily on the surface, slowing down its natural functions. You want to know that your skin is being helped, not hampered by a product, that it will regain its natural lines when you've stopped smiling, whistling, eating, pouting . . . just look at all the actions that work against your skin. It needs all the help you can give it, expecially around the eyes and the upper lip area. Your neck, too, is subject to dryness; it is, in fact, the first place that shows signs of aging. When the occasion permits, wear a scarf prettily tied around your throat to protect this delicate skin.

NOTE: *The area around your eyes, the upper lip area, and your neck should always be protected whether the rest of your face is* PLUS *or* MINUS.

MAKEUP: WHAT YOUR MOTHER MIGHT NOT HAVE TOLD YOU

There is nothing quite as exciting or magical as the first time a young girl applies makeup. Aside from being a lot of fun to use, makeup can enhance your looks, but it should do more. It should *protect* and work to help keep the pH (perfect) balance of your skin. This is why you should never reach for a makeup that covers or masks your face—this is a lesson you can teach your mother if she's still wearing a product that she thinks of as a base or a foundation. This heavy formulation will always look and feel artificial. A MINUS skin won't derive any benefits from its use and a PLUS skin can suffer clogged pores because of it.

The only foundation for beauty is your skin itself and all the products you apply to it must promote and aid a beautiful, clear complexion.

When I hear the word makeup, I immediately think of a natural look that flatters you. Makeup can improve your features, but it can't physically alter them. The most common mistake made by young girls is using makeup to try to make them look like someone else, often a model in a photograph. I understand that a model can look strikingly attractive in a magazine—without an eye-catching appearance, she would never capture your attention. But the very same model would probably not dream of wearing such a contrived face outside of the artificial setup of a studio.

An artist's makeup tricks improve on a model's beauty artfully. The angle at which she is photographed can conceal the artificiality of his handiwork. But in a natural, real-life setting, *you* are seen from all angles and this kind of makeup technique would be obvious to everyone.

Understand makeup's limitations and learn to use it wisely.

The first item many girls seek out is lipstick. If you're thinking that your lips need special care, you're right. You smile, you lick your lips, you purse them in a hundred different ways and they need to be protected. But a lip gloss that provides a shine is not enough to soften and heal them if, for example, they're chapped. Lipsticks don't often offer the soothing protection you want. Look for a petroleum jelly product if you can't get my LIP SARTINIZER, which was developed with the chapped lip problem in mind.

The upper lip area, the area around your eyes, and your neck can benefit from the proper daywear preparation. You want to use a nongreasy lubricant such as my SKIN PASTE which nourishes MINUS skin and prevents

wrinkling by keeping skin pliant and protected from the environment.

Your nose—an area which is PLUS for almost everyone—needs the right astringent to normalize the flow of oil and prevent the pores from becoming clogged.

Read through chapter 4, "Making Makeup Work for You," to find out how to choose your makeup and how to apply it. You want to select the preparations that will help your own skin type—you can't use products haphazardly and expect your skin to stay lovely. I must caution you against using makeup preparations that are formulated with iridescence. They can create an irritation you can certainly do without. If your eyelids are not subject to allergic reactions, you might use an iridescent eye shadow—the only exception to my rule.

I have left color choice up to you because your coloring is individual. You needn't limit yourself to a narrow range of selection but do strive for excellence. Avoid loud, offensive colors. Remember, too, that the more moderate shades are usually the ones that complement and harmonize with your skin tone. Let makeup work its magic in subtle ways.

The right rouge or blusher, the right eye shadow, in both medium and color appropriate for you, can make you look prettier than you already are and won't hurt your skin in the least. This is true for women of all ages: *makeup should be selected according to your skin's needs and not because of attractive packaging or well-advertised promises.*

NIGHTTIME CARE

Experimenting with makeup is one of the pleasures of being a woman, but as with all play, there must come a time when the playthings are put back on the shelf. For you, this is in the evening, before you go to sleep, and it involves thoroughly cleansing your face. Going to sleep with the day's soil and makeup on your skin is out of the question!

Neither is it right, or necessary, to sleep with cream on your face—and unless your skin is BALANCED or MINUS, cream based preparations aren't for you. They can, however, help BALANCED or MINUS skin and the MINUS areas of the oily face: the area around the eyes, the upper lip, and the neck. A well-formulated preparation needs only fifteen minutes to work, regardless of your age.

You may want, if you are eighteen or over, to start using a nourishing emollient such as my SUPERFATTED CREAM after cleansing in the evening. Remember not to use this on your nose, as it has enough oil of its own. Tissue off the cream as described in chapter 3 and you won't ever have to worry about greasy bedsheets.

When you reach your thirties and forties, you may wish to use a richer cream—I'll tell you all about that in the next chapter: I don't want to give you too much to think about too soon.

I hope I've let you know how simple it is to plan ahead. A practical routine and a little forethought can go a long way to a more beautiful you. You might like to read chapter 10, "Take Care," to understand and prevent the effects summer and winter, good days and bad, can have on your skin. And always remember my rule for young skin:

It is important for the future to consider your face now.

7.

Approaching the Vintage Years

Lovely looking skin is an asset at any age. And isn't it nice to know that as you get older, your skin can look younger? If you begin to take the proper care of your complexion now, you needn't worry about showing your age as you approach your thirties, your forties, your fifties, and even your sixties. Of course you'll want to pay careful attention to your body as well —good grooming includes keeping a youthful figure.

In the first chapter of this book, I told you that skin care includes *protection* and *prevention*. Now is the time to consider adding both these elements to your program. Those with MINUS skin especially must think of protect-

ing their skin throughout the day in order to prevent those signs of aging that we are all so aware of—the expression lines that can so easily become wrinkles.

Those with PLUS skin will have to protect the dry areas of their face, usually the area around the eyes, the upper lip area, and the neck. If you have oily skin, you will have to guard against excesses of oil that laden and cause your skin to fall into creases and furrows.

Why does our appearance change as we get older?

There are three major factors that cause our face to show age. *Gravity—*

which we all learned about in school, when we were too young to fully grasp its meaning and its consequences—is one of the culprits. The gravital pull of the earth causes your face to sag over the years by pulling the flesh off your bone structure. The use of heavily formulated preparations can help gravity ravage your appearance; this is why you should never rely on heavy moisturizers to renew your skin's texture: most of those available across today's cosmetic counters work against the very benefits they seek to promote.

The *everyday stress of life,* both the good and the bad stresses, cause expression lines. These can deepen and become permanent, particularly if you have a MINUS skin that does not have the pliancy needed to regain its natural look after a frown or a smile.

Perhaps the most damaging aging factor is the one that we have the most control over: *exposure to the elements* such as the sun, the cold, and the wind. Prolonged exposure to the sun can dry our natural lubricating oils, severely reducing the skin's pliability. It is the pliability or elasticity that is so very vital to the preservation of soft, supple, youthful-looking skin. Elasticity can help your face resist the pull of the earth. It can bring about the release of expression lines, enabling our skin to ease back into its natural state. It can compensate for a poor bone structure which would otherwise cause the skin to fall into folds.

Your bone structure plays a part in the aging process. Broad cheekbones and a strong jawline will keep your flesh in good form for a longer time. A weak bone structure can cause it to show age prematurely.

If the structure of your teeth is rounded rather than broad, not providing enough support, your upper lip area will have an increased tendency to crevice.

In these instances, *working to keep your skin elastic will help your skin remain youthful and healthy.*

Approaching the vintage years needn't be a traumatic time in your life. It is important to understand the changes that are taking place and to be aware of the warning signals. This is true for those who have just begun to mature as well as for those who have already started the vintage years.

The kind of skin primarily affected by the aging process is the MINUS skin, be it the dry areas of the PLUS face (the area around the eyes, the upper lip area, and the neck) or the overall dryness of the MINUS face.

However, the PLUS face can show a kind of aging which I would like to clarify right away, before you start using the wrong preparations, hoping to chase away these wrinkles.

When the skin is overly laden with oils, it becomes very heavy and sluggish. If the skin is thick and these oils cannot pass through to the surface, the skin becomes saturated with fatty acids which cause it to fall into crevices. Most noticeable and frequently apparent are the *furrows* on the forehead, in between the eyebrows, and the parentheses lines around the mouth.

The answer for this problem is not to apply cream to these areas because these are not dry skin wrinkles. The additional fatty acids found in the emollient preparations would aggravate the problem, causing the lines to deepen and possibly creating blemishes by further clogging the pores.

You want to normalize the skin by having it excrete its oils more rapidly. This in turn will lighten the skin's texture, insuring enough elasticity to release the lines, smoothing these areas. Follow the skin care program set forth for this skin type in chapter 5, "Problem Skin: Breakthrough or Breakout."

If the area around your eyes, your upper lip area, and your neck are dry and unblemished, you'll need to give these areas special attention to keep them pliant. Read about the kind of care these areas require in the section below called "the MINUS skin system."

The MINUS skin wrinkling is quite different than that of a PLUS skin crevicing. A dry skin that is of a thin texture like parchment paper will notice a fine network of wrinkling. The thicker skins will show deeper wrinkling such as the forehead parallel lines, the frown lines between the eyebrows, and the half circles around the mouth.

Any kind of wrinkling or crevicing will detract from our appearance and we must work to prevent these from occurring at all costs. When I say this, I want you to know that I'm not referring to financial costs, but rather to the amount of constructive time you spend on your skin. Hundreds of dollars' worth of creams and other preparations won't bring results if they're chosen and used incorrectly.

On the other hand, the extra five minutes it takes for a nourishing cream to work in the morning can make all the difference when you go outdoors. Even when staying at home, you'll want to use the proper preparations to protect against steam heat or your air conditioning, both of which can adversely affect your skin.

After going out, take the time to make your skin feel comfortable once you return home, especially if you've been exposed to a cold winter day or to the strong rays of the sun (and remember, you don't have to be sunbathing for the sun to reach your delicate facial skin).

I know that five or ten minutes is little enough time to devote to your complexion. And when you begin to see results—and receive compliments!—you'll think so as well.

THE −3 AND −4 SKIN

The −3 skin is an uncomfortable skin that has begun to show strong signs of age.

The −4 skin is the most advanced stage of dryness, a condition already characterized by wrinkling and crevicing.

What I want you to do is to bring your −3 or −4 skin to a −2 or, possibly, a −1 condition, in which case the dryness is controlled, the suppleness maintained.

Just as neglected skin can easily worsen, a protected and nurtured skin can be improved.

The first step toward helping your complexion is beginning my program which uses preparations to soothe it and keep it comfortable. The constant use of a mineral oil complex will nourish as it cleanses the skin. A treatment cream will be used as well—there are many available and I want you to become discerning. The following descriptions are of the two creams or *carriers,* formulated with fatty acids, that you will need to use, when and where:

A NOURISHING CREAM: This is a light-textured, silken cream. You don't want a cream that "vanishes"—if it disappears, it can't be doing much good!

This cream can be used on the MINUS face (except the nose area as it can be subject to clogged pores) and on the dry areas of the PLUS face (under the eyes, above the upper lip, and on the neck, if these areas are dry and unblemished).

A COLLAGEN (PROTEIN) CREAM: This is formulated in a heavier carrier for areas that tend to be excessively dry and uncomfortable, that wrinkle easily.

If you have MINUS skin and are in your thirties, you should begin to use this cream under the eyes, above the upper lip, and on the neck, as these areas may require a richer cream than the rest of your face. Its use can be extended to the entire MINUS face, except the nose area if oily, as you approach forty and beyond, if your skin belongs to the —4 category.

Those with PLUS skin will limit the use of the protein cream to the area under the eyes, the upper lip area, and the neck if these are excessively dry and unblemished.

THE MINUS SKIN SYSTEM FOR —3 AND —4 SKIN

In the morning and, optionally, in the evening, before dressing:

1. Saturate a piece of sterilized cotton from your roll with a mineral oil complex (CLEANSING OIL) and gently cleanse your face, omitting your nose as it can be subject to clogged pores. Cleanse the right side of your face first, using a sweeping movement from the inner corner of the eye extending outward over the cheek and jaw area.

Use the reverse side of the cotton and then turn it inside out for the maximum four-side usage. Repeat this for the left side of your face. Move to the center of your forehead and cleanse the area to the right, then to the left of the center.

With clean cotton, go across the chin. Cleanse your neck from the center to the right, the center to the left.

Use fresh cotton as needed. Do not blot.

2. Saturate a clean piece of cotton with astringent (CLEAR ASTRINGENT) and cleanse the nose, being sure to cleanse in the curve of the nostrils and beneath the tip.

3. Fill your basin or bowl with warm water. Wet your face and hands. Lather your face with your wet fatty acid based soap (SUPERFATTED SOAP) and make a separate lather in your hands. Work both lathers gently into your skin. With the oil residue, the soap creates an emulsion to soften your skin.

4. Holding your elbows out to the sides, rinse your face with the water in the basin for a total of *fifteen* times to derive the full treatment benefits of the emulsion.

5. Dry your face with a soft, clean towel.

6. Smooth a light nourishing cream (SUPERFATTED CREAM) on your face and neck, omitting your nose, as it can be subject to clogged pores. Leave it on for *ten* minutes. Gently blot off the excess with a tissue.

7. Saturate a piece of cotton with your mineral oil complex (CLEANSING OIL) and apply it to your face, omitting your nose. Blot dry with a tissue.

8. Using your index finger, dot a small amount of your emollient based daywear preparation (SKIN PASTE) on your face, omitting the nose, as it can be subject to clogged pores.

First apply the preparation to the right half of your face, starting under the eye. Continue to your cheek area, using your middle finger to smooth it into your skin.

Repeat the application to the left side of your face, including the upper lip area, the chin, the neck and, lastly, using the smallest amount, the forehead. Blot with a tissue.

9. Follow with cream rouge, face powder, eye makeup, and lipstick as described in chapter 4, "Making Makeup Work for You."

In the evening, before retiring, after you have removed your lipstick and eye makeup as described in chapter 3, "The World's Best (and Simplest) Skin Care System," follow the morning routine through step 5. Continue with:

6. *For the —3 skin:* smooth a light nourishing cream (SUPERFATTED CREAM) on your face and neck, omitting the nose, as it can be subject to clogged pores. A collagen cream (HEAVY NIGHT CREAM) can be applied to the under-eye, upper-lip, and neck areas if excessively dry. Leave on for *fifteen* minutes. Blot it off with tissue.

For the —4 skin: smooth on a collagen cream (HEAVY NIGHT CREAM) on your face and neck, omitting your nose, as it can be subject to clogged pores. Leave it on for *fifteen* minutes. Blot it off with tissue.

NOTE: My heavier carrier, called HEAVY NIGHT CREAM, is a rich protein cream formulated to soften excessively dry skin. Although it is called a "night" cream and is used before retiring, it should, like any cream you use, be blotted off before you go to sleep. A good cream does not have to be left on overnight to be effective.

Additionally, you can treat your skin to two treatments I have found to be beneficial to the MINUS skin, the MILK BATH and the OIL COMPRESS.

THE MILK BATH

This simple treatment can greatly benefit a dry skin far more than any so-called beauty mask. It is especially good when used before going out in the evening, to give your face a beautifying lift.

After following your routine through step 5, continue with these steps:

1. Place a half cup of whole milk (chock-full of fatty acids that your skin needs) in a small receptacle.

2. Dip a piece of cotton in the milk and dab it on your face. Keep dabbing on the milk for a total of three minutes. Let it set on your face for five minutes longer.

3. Rinse off the milk with lukewarm water and follow with your makeup steps.

THE OIL COMPRESS

This treatment might be most conveniently followed after your last cleansing routine in the evening, before retiring, but it is most beneficial at any time. Follow your routine through the final step 6, but don't blot off the application of cream. Continue with these steps for a nourishing compress:

1. Separate pieces of cotton from your roll into thin layers. Make each piece just short of the size of the areas you'll be using them on. Remember that the nose is to be omitted, as it can be subject to clogged pores.

2. Saturate one half of each piece of cotton, one at a time, with a mineral oil complex (CLEANSING OIL). Fold the dry half over this to saturate it. (This step prevents any waste of oil.)

3. Stretch each piece over the area you wish to cover. The cotton for each cheek should begin under the eye and extend over the cheek to the jawline. Use separate pieces for the upper lip, the chin, the neck, and the forehead.

4. Leave the compresses in place for *fifteen* minutes. As you remove the cotton, use it to wipe off all excess cream. Blot any that remains by placing a tissue against your skin, smoothing it with your index finger and lifting it off.

Once you've placed your fragile skin on my program, you'll never again have to worry about the changing seasons and their effect on your complexion. Your skin will stay soft and supple every day, through winter and summer alike.

8

Body Essentials

The feeling of luxury that comes from pampering ourselves is a joy we can all savor. Pampering needn't be a frivolous use of time; after all, it is just personal hygiene accomplished with flair. The care is essential to our bodies, the flair nurtures our soul.

Bathing daily is a necessity and the bath can be made special without much additional outlay of time. At the other end of the spectrum, many pursuits that we most likely think of as pampering—such as having a facial—may give a sense of luxury for the moment, but are not part of a follow-through program which assures accumulative benefits for the future.

In each of the sections of this chapter, I'll tell you how to make everyday essential pamperings and which occasional splurges are best forgotten.

YOUR FACE

FACIALS

When many women want to feel pampered and fussed over, their first inclination is to check in at their nearby facial parlor and wait for their number to be called. I've already told you how I feel about this practice; now I'll tell you why.

Although the idea of a restful hour filled with beautifying benefits is very appealing, the results of these brief, erratic encounters are unfortunately very limited, if not altogether nonexistent. More importantly, you run the risk of aftereffects which would be far more detrimental to your facial beauty than not having touched your complexion in the first place.

If, for instance, you put your face in the hands of an operator who doesn't quite understand the physiology of skin or who doesn't have much experience in dealing with the individual nature of your skin, you might be in trouble. She might use materials that would clog the pores of a PLUS skin. Even though you may feel relaxed by the pitter-patter of fingertips smoothing on creams, you may not need them! Creams can cause already clogged pores to develop into blemishes. If you are subject to blackheads, these can become aggravated. And even if the operator were to remove the clogs, she may follow that procedure with products that would reclog them.

MINUS skin might not be adversely affected by the use of creams, but the slapping and pulling action often administered can result in a loss of elasticity; these massage-like actions can engender the breakdown of fatty tissues needed to cushion your skin and keep it on the bone structure. If you're lucky enough to have this support, you won't want it damaged or lessened in any way.

My strongest complaint with the once-in-a-while facial is that it plays no part in your thorough skin care program. You need to think in terms of a system that will help your skin today and every other day because it is followed *today and every other day*, not just when you're in the mood. Without a daily program, you're defeating your purpose and wasting your money.

If it is the restful feeling you're looking for, you can achieve a look of serenity by taking a short rest in your own darkened bedroom after you've gone through your cleansing routine, perhaps while you treat yourself to a WHITE ASTRINGENT COMPRESS (for those with oily skin) or an OIL COMPRESS (for those with dry skin).

FACE MASKS

I am not in favor of the types of masks that are so prevalent these days. Most offer results that are very short-lived and which can, accumulatively, cause more damage than benefits.

High on the list of those to be avoided are masks that *tighten* the skin for a short amount of time. These include homemade or other preparations that contain the white of eggs. By tightening and later relaxing the skin, you loosen the scarf cuticle and suffer a loss of elasticity. If you've thought of using a mask of this type because your skin lacks elasticity, know that its use can bring about an even greater loss.

Masks that *swell* the skin, giving the impression of plumping the wrinkles, again for only a few hours, are not of any benefit either. These contain an irritant which causes your expression lines to diminish temporarily—and that is not good for your skin.

Masks that you whip up from *natural ingredients* such as yogurt, cucumber, banana, and avocado, to name a few, might be fun to do, but won't give you the kind of lasting results you should be looking for. My feeling is that we'd be much better off eating these delicious, healthy foods (of course, if you have a PLUS skin, no avocados, please).

For those with MINUS skin: treat yourself to the MILK BATH I described in chapter 7, "Approaching the Vintage Years."

For those with ALLERGIC or SENSI-TIVE skin: try the TEA BAG TREATMENT found in chapter 5, "Problem Skin: Breakthrough or Breakout."

For those with PLUS skin, I would like to suggest one type of mask that can be very beneficial, the MUD MASK.

Mud is a healing property and draws out inflammation, but, as a mask, it must be prepared fresh. The premixed types packaged in tubes are not to be used because the format necessitates the addition of an emollient to ease it into the tube and no emollients should ever be used on a PLUS skin!

In the forties, mud imported from Italy had to be heated to be applied. Various temperature testings on the wrist made it an annoying procedure at times. But today's preparations can be mixed cold and are easy to use once a week for the +1 and +2 skin, twice a week for those with +3 and +4 skin.

Rosewater can be used for a fresh, fragrant feeling after the above treatments or simply after you've cleansed your face thoroughly, before applying your daywear preparation. Use it generously, with cotton.

You can buy rosewater at your pharmacy or have the pharmacist make it up for you. Don't look for products that contain glycerine or any other ingredients. You want rosewater in its pure state.

Your lips can benefit from a good salve used consistently.

A few years ago, my son, Cary, had lips that were constantly chapped. Because the problem wasn't being relieved by any products on the market, I began developing my own preparation. After several formulations, the salve we call the LIP SARTINIZER was the one preparation that healed Cary's lips.

We put the salve in a small container that Cary could take with him to school and found that it worked so well we decided to include it in our complete line of preparations.

Word spread quickly among my clients and one day I received a call from Mamie Eisenhower, at the time that the General was so ill at Walter Reed Hospital. Mrs. Eisenhower told me that she had heard of my lip salve from one of our California clients and asked that I send some to General Eisenhower. I still have the very nice "thank you" note that I received from her.

YOUR HAIR

FOR YOUR CROWNING GLORY: A HOT OIL TREATMENT

This treatment is especially helpful to those who have a dry, flaky scalp. Follow these steps twice a week before shampooing:

1. Heat about half a cup of olive oil in a saucepan, being careful that the oil doesn't burn. It shouldn't be too hot to touch.

2. Separate your hair into sections and rub the warmed oil into your scalp using cotton.

3. Take a turkish towel and saturate it with hot water. Wring it out completely and wrap it around your head.

4. Repeat the above step three or four times as the towel cools. The heat from the towel helps the oil lubricate your scalp.

5. Thoroughly wash the oil out of your hair and scalp with your shampoo.

UNWANTED FACIAL HAIR

Heavy hair growth or, in some cases, a lighter fuzz *around the jawline and the sides on the neck* can present a problem for those with PLUS skin. Oily secretions which cling to the hair shafts and harden cannot be readily discharged. Nature then steps in by creating an inflammation to soften the accumulation and help it pass through.

If your facial hair growth is heavy enough to create an inflammatory condition that reoccurs, I would suggest having the hair shoots removed through electrolysis. Prior to having the hair eliminated, make sure that the clogs and any infection have been cleared because, if not, the heat of the needle used may cause an eruption. Electrolysis will assist in clearing the skin of the blemishes caused by the hair growth.

Your electrolysist must be well recommended by either your physician or your skin care specialist—you can't pick a number out of the telephone book and expect the best possible results. If the practitioner is knowledgeable, and has proved this by achieving excellent results, you can be assured that there are few, if any, risks involved.

I must tell you in all honesty that this procedure can be painful. Often, you can elect to have the unwanted hair removed little by little, to acclimate yourself to the process, which involves destroying the hair with a small charge of electricity administered through the needle to the papilla.

To those who are not bothered by excessive facial hair, this might sound harsh. But to the person who is constantly plagued by pustules caused by the hirsute condition, electrolysis might just be the answer.

Hair growth *above the upper lip* is a common complaint. Unfortunately, most of the methods employed to deal with it can be far more harmful, in the long run, than the presence of hair.

Waxing is the most damaging procedure of all because by pulling and stretching the skin, it can accelerate the loss of elasticity in an area that is often already prone to wrinkling.

Shaving can create stubble and often a stronger hair growth. The use of depilatories can create a reddened, sensitive reaction. Neither of these should be looked on as a solution.

Bleaching is a possible alternative, though it does not always effectively hide the problem and must be frequently repeated.

The only sure solution is electrolysis which, as explained above, can at times be painful. You will have to allow for short visits, as even the electrolysist won't want to work extensively on this area for any great length of time. But, by being consistent, the hair growth will eventually be cleared.

TWEEZING

Few of us are satisfied with the shape of our eyebrows and reach for the tweezers to pluck before understanding what our eyebrows can do for our appearance and how to shape them properly.

Brush your eyebrows fully, shaping them to the natural contour of your eye. What you want to do first is remove all the stray hairs, both above and below the natural arch of your brow. You may then decide to trim the eyebrow if it appears too heavy. Follow these steps for a smooth removal of eyebrow hairs:

1. Cleanse the area with cotton that has been saturated with astringent (CLEAR ASTRINGENT). Blot dry.

Using the same cotton, wipe clean your tweezers, then dry them.

2. With one hand, hold the skin firmly as you tweeze the straggling hairs, following the direction they grow in. Remove one hair at a time so that you can gauge your progress.

3. When you have finished tweezing, apply my well-shaken WHITE ASTRINGENT to each area tweezed, to avoid any infection or inflammation from ingrown hairs.

UNWANTED BODY HAIR

Under the arms, on the forearms, and on your legs, is hair almost all women want to remove for aesthetic reasons. There are various ways of going about this.

Shaving with a razor is a frequently used method, but one which, as I am sure you know, must be repeated—often at the first sign of stubble that appears soon after. Knicks and bruises are the hazards that accompany this technique. The underarm area is small enough to be handled with a razor, but your legs require far more time and patience.

Waxing your legs can cause capillary breakage if these blood vessels are fragile. These won't disappear.

Once again, I must suggest that electrolysis is the simple way to eliminate the problem; the others are a halfway measure as they merely postpone it.

I want you to know that I am talking from my own experience; electrolysis is the solution I chose and it worked. During my earlier career as a dancer, I found, to my chagrin, that the static electricity from the hair fuzz on my legs caused my chiffon gowns to cling rather than float gracefully. At that time, I started shaving and found, to my despair, that I began to acquire a strong stubble which had to be shaved daily! It wasn't until much later that I discovered the benefits of electrolysis and my good friend Gemma Lama, who solved my problem in short order. I am truly grateful that I have never again had to touch a razor and that my legs are smoother than ever.

The number of visits you'll need to have your hair fully removed depends on the thickness and strength of the growth. But remember, you'll never need to use a razor again, either!

EXERCISING

FACIAL EXERCISES

There are definite drawbacks to facial exercises. They can constrict the blood vessels or capillaries; the flow of oxygen is then restricted—not at all healthy. Developed facial muscles can be quite unattractive as well.

To cite an example, a woman from Detroit, who later became a client of mine, had so diligently exercised that she developed bunches of muscles on either side of her mouth. These were so pronounced that her friends nicknamed her "Squirrel."

Using my own special technique of muscle toning enabled me to eliminate these bulges within a few visits. The results were so dramatic that I soon had a large Michigan clientele.

I am now hoping to make this process available on a larger scale, in the near future.

BODY EXERCISES

No matter what your age, you should pay careful attention to keeping your body in condition. Body muscles, unlike the smaller ones of your face, will sustain a daily exercise routine, keeping them elastic and keeping you trim and healthy. Vigorous exercise also increases the amount of oxygen our blood carries to our skin cells. Fresh air accomplishes this as well, making brisk walking outdoors an ideal exercise. Smoking, by the way, reduces the efficacy of the all-important supply of oxygen.

The best at-home exercise is *walking on all fours.* This uses every muscle and exercises your entire body. Start with five minutes a day and slowly work up to ten or fifteen.

Stretching is a good exercise as well. Think of the way a cat stretches, waking every limb separately. Stretch to reach for a book, stretch when you stand up. It is a relaxing action as well as an exercising one.

A body massage is helpful to your circulation, but I don't recommend the strenuous type of massage with the goal of reducing fatty tissue in mind. It would be far more beneficial to rely on a physical exercise program combined with the proper diet to lose both the pounds and inches.

THE BATH

For those with PLUS skin who notice a breakout on their chest, shoulders, or back, the bath can be a corrective treatment.

For those with MINUS or dry body skin, the bath can be a soothing, softening treatment.

There are a multitude of bath enhancers—bath oils, bubble baths, water softeners—available in numerous fragrances. But you mustn't be tempted by pretty packages if the product inside can harm your skin.

Perfumed soaps should be used only as sachets to freshen your drawers. As cleansing agents, these can be very drying and, on some skins, can cause an allergic reaction. *Any kind of scented product must be used with caution as it might be irritating.* Those with dry skin will benefit from the use of their fatty acid based soap. Those with an oily skin, prone to breaking out, will use their anti-bacterial, anti-acne soap.

Bath oil is recommended for those with dry skin. If you have oily skin, prone to breaking out, do not use this product: you don't need any additional oil on your skin surface.

Bubble bath is purely for fun. However, certain bubble baths might contain perfume or other ingredients that can be irritating. Use this product with caution.

A rich *body lotion* should always be used after your bath on skin that tends to be dry, particularly your arms and legs, but never on skin that is prone to blemishes.

If your back, your shoulders, your chest, or any other external part of your body suffers from clogged pores and blemishes, follow your bath with my SKIN APPLICATION and WHITE ASTRINGENT as directed in chapter 5, "Problem Skin: Breakthrough or Breakout." You can cleanse the area with astringent (CLEAR ASTRINGENT) in the morning and evening (as well as before you bathe), then follow with my two other preparations to promote healing.

A well-formulated *hand cream* will nourish your hands as well as your feet, your elbows, and knees. This

should be of a heavier formulation than your body lotion. The product I developed, simply called HAND CREAM, has been a favorite of many of my clients, most notably the Duchess of Windsor.

Your feet deserve added, special care and having a *pedicure* can be a most wonderful lift on an ordinary day and a miracle cure on a hurried, tense one. This gives a delightful, pampered feeling but again should be thought of as a must. A pedicure can make your entire body feel better. I suggest getting a professional foot massage-treatment once a month from a good chiropodist—don't wait until you need him badly. Your feet should be especially nurtured because of all the work you ask of them.

After your bath is a good time to apply your *deodorant*. Aerosal spray deodorants can be irritating to you and damaging to the environment: try a cream or other type to determine which is best for you.

Bath powder is a lovely finishing agent and can protect against chafing, too.

The proper use of these products can make your bath a relaxing and beneficial time.

SLEEP

The proper amount of rest is a beauty essential, for a look of serenity on your face as well as for your mental and physical well-being. But too much sleep isn't good as you get older; you'll want to keep your body functioning for longer periods to increase your circulation and that means sleeping less. After the age of sixty or, in some cases, even earlier, five or six hours would be enough. But if you truly need your eight hours, by all means take them. The best amount of sleep is the time it takes for you to feel rested.

If you find that taking a nap in the afternoon or early evening is necessary, then do it.

Plan your day to avoid last-minute stress and aggravation.

Don't lie awake at night wondering about the problems of the next day. Try to forget them.

Organize your mind and you can organize your life and enjoy a greater harmony each day.

9

Skin Nutrition

There is a variation of the old adage that says you are what you eat, one that most definitely holds true: your skin reflects what you eat. A healthy, BALANCED complexion won't suffer an adverse reaction to any food, but other skins will most assuredly tattle on a poor diet.

Equally true is the fact that certain foods encourage a clear complexion while others are downright destructive to the PLUS or acne-prone skins. There have been medical reports stating that foods such as chocolate, fried dishes, soda fountain concoctions, and the like have no adverse effect on problem skin. In regard to this, I must say that the fact that these foods contain little or no nutritional value is reason enough to avoid them; that they can result in blemishes, for those with acne-prone skin, and aggravate the skin condition of those already suffering with acne gives you a second concrete reason to cross them off your list.

There are some very nutritive foods that have an adverse reaction on the PLUS skins as well. Shellfish, a rich source of protein, is also a rich source of minerals which can lead to an irritation or blemish.

Certain medications, such as cough syrup, sleeping pills, and tranquilizers which may contain codeine to produce a quieting effect, have been found to cause a blemish on SENSITIVE and ALLERGIC skins in particular.

A BALANCED skin has sufficient strength to resist any systemic reaction from a food or drug; the irritant in the product will pass through waste channels. However, a vulnerable skin will show a breakout as the irritant tries to pass through the pores of the face.

The following foods have a tendency to further aggravate an oily or PLUS skin and must be avoided:

Fried or greasy foods of all kinds, including Chinese food, fast food chain offerings such as fried chicken, French fries, fried fish.

Foods with a high oil content, including mayonnaise, salad dressings, avocados; *oils,* including vegetable, olive, peanut, sesame.

Shellfish: lobster, crab, shrimp, clams, scallops, mussels, oysters.

Starches: pasta, potatoes, rice, flour and flour based products, including puddings, cake, breads, cookies.

Dairy products such as butter; whole milk (this contains fatty acids), SUBSTITUTE skim milk; rich runny cheeses such as Camembert, Brie, the blue cheeses, SUBSTITUTE cottage cheese or hard cheeses such as Swiss or American. Additionally, you'll want to limit your intake of eggs.

Cocoa and cola and their derivatives, including cola flavored beverages, chocolate, syrups, candies.

Sugar, including white, brown, refined. SUBSTITUTE honey.

There are a great variety of foods that please the PLUS skin and promote clear, healthy skin. These are:

Meat and *Poultry.*

Fresh fish: broiled, poached, or steamed, NOT fried.

Fresh fruits, preferably stewed to reduce the sugar content. (Those with ALLERGIC skin must avoid strawberries.)

Fresh vegetables, cooked or raw.

Cooked cereals: farina, oatmeal.

Clear broths and vegetable soup.

Those with MINUS skin will benefit from the preferred list and can also include whole milk and butter (dairy products) as well as the oils restricted to those with oily skin. However, you should avoid bleached flours (SUBSTITUTE whole wheat) and sugars (SUBSTITUTE honey).

NOTES ON NUTRITION

Water.

Drinking plentiful amounts of water is good for those with PLUS skin and MINUS skin alike. We can all benefit from eight glasses of water a day. This may sound like a lot at first, but remember that you don't have to drink it all at once. One eight-ounce glass every two hours will spread the intake over the course of your day and evening. Water encourages a better complexion.

Vitamins.

We are all concerned with getting the proper nutrition and often, when we feel we aren't, we seek out vitamins. I would like to suggest that you discuss your specific needs with your physician before you reach for megadoses of vitamins.

Anyone can benefit from one daily multiple vitamin. If you have +3 or +4 skin, however, you will want to avoid those that have additional minerals added as these can create a blemish or irritation.

Enzymes.

Fresh vegetables, especially good for everyone, contain enzymes that we all need. However, vegetables are often treated with additives (e.g., insecticides) that we don't want. An effective way of ridding the vegetable of the additives while preserving the enzymes is to process it through a juice extractor. The additives and the pulp are separated from the juice and the enzymes for a healthful drink.

Alcohol.

The excessive indulgence of alcohol can result in a variety of adverse effects. Too much alcohol can cause a form of edema or swelling of your skin, giving you a pudgy look. Other people might get a discoloration on the skin surface, the reddened result of diffused capillaries (this can, of course, occur for other reasons, but it is a frequent sign of alcohol abuse).

Dieting.

Yes, a poor diet can have a damaging effect on your skin. This is why you should select a balanced daily intake of food from the preferred list. Dieting to lose pounds must be carefully done. Fad dieting and fasting can be as harmful to your body as it is to its outer organ, your skin. Your system will take what it needs from your vital organs, damaging them needlessly.

Enjoy everything, but in smaller quantities—that is the key to successful, painless weight loss while you keep your beautiful complexion.

10.

Take Care

When I am called on by beauty editors for advice on skin care, the subject they are often concerned with is how to restore your skin from one season to another. Correcting the ravages of summer each year is a trial which, with only a little forethought, could be crossed off your list of worries. Why not plan ahead, at the beginning of the summer, to prevent the damages which are so hard to correct? Remember too that after thoughtlessly exposing yourself to the sun in the summer, you'll have not only to compensate for its ravages, but will also suffer, unprepared, the assault of winter exposure, which can make the skin even drier.

All skins need special care to maintain their elasticity and thereby stay youthful, but there's no need to sound the alarm in early September. With the proper care, you can slip into each season without any problem.

The sun, though by far the most dangerous, is only one of the elements you must guard against. Exposure to winter's cold, indoor temperature changes due to heating and air conditioning, stress—both good and bad, drugs we take can all effect your skin. I want you to take care, so that the complexion you've worked so hard to achieve in the earlier chapters will not deteriorate.

SUN SENSE

Because exposure to the sun can be so very aging and because we so love to enjoy it regardless, I want to explore this subject with you thoroughly.

Why is the sun harmful?

Because it can dry out your natural oils at a faster rate than usual. The MINUS skin which cannot supplement any loss of oil from its precious stock becomes taut. A taut skin is not supple enough to release expression lines and the lines deepen.

If you have suffered the drying consequences of the sun, you must take the proper steps now. Those with MINUS or BALANCED skin will want to follow the soothing routine for excessively dry skin outlined in chapter 7, "Approaching the Vintage Years."

Though a PLUS skin can withstand some of the drying effects of the sun, too much exposure can result in a parched top layer which traps the oils underneath the surface. This condition is called the COMBINATION skin and must be treated with that special program outlined in chapter 5, "Problem Skin: Breakthrough or Breakout."

Once you have begun the necessary constructive program, you will want to return to this chapter to learn how to *prevent* the condition from recurring.

No matter which type of skin you have—PLUS, MINUS, SENSITIVE, or ALLERGIC—it must be protected before you expose it to the sun. And even though you might be using the proper preparations to accomplish this job, you mustn't take the sun indiscriminately. No one can bask in the sunshine for hours on end, even if you think you have the rare kind of skin that "can take it." Even PLUS skin should not sunbathe more than a few hours at a time—and only after gradually acclimating your skin to the sun—and no skin should ever be exposed between the hours of noon and three when the sun is at its peak.

Very fair skins must be especially cautious about lying in the sun. Start with five minutes at a time and gradually work up to fifteen minutes. You should be particularly wary of exposure if you have a pre-tendency to skin cancer—a dry skin which would normally use an oil based sun preparation will, in this case, need a greaseless one that will block out rather than attract the rays of the sun.

Olive-toned skins may take a little more sun, as these skins are hardier and usually can supplement any loss of oil.

There are special guidelines for those with MINUS skin and those with PLUS.

If you have a SENSITIVE skin which tends to be dry, follow the MINUS suggestions.

If you have an ALLERGIC skin which shows an adverse reaction to cream and oil based products, follow the PLUS suggestions.

SUN SENSE
FOR MINUS SKIN

It may feel delightful and delicious to bask in the warm sun, but that old adage of having to "pay the piper" was never so true. MINUS skin that is subjected to the damaging rays of the sun might acquire an attractive tan, but the harmful aftereffects will be noticeable long after that deep color has faded. Why? Because after the age of seventeen, our cellular renewal process slows down. The cells cannot renew themselves at a rate rapid enough to compensate for the drying effect of the sun. The lost moisture results in a loss of elasticity which in turn results in the permanency of expression lines. The more exposure you take, the greater the loss of elasticity, the deeper the lines.

At any age you will need to use a rich oil for tanning, such as my BRONZING OIL formulated with the richest oils available as well as a sunscreen. Your nose area will require a greaseless, liquid sunscreen (never an oil or cream) to keep it from burning; my preparation is called SUN LOTION.

As you turn eighteen, you must begin limiting your intake of sunshine and begin protecting your delicate complexion so that a slightly MINUS skin doesn't become more advanced, and more difficult to soothe and correct.

Your bronzing product should be used on your body as well as your face to keep it soft and supple too.

Starting at age twenty, you'll want to take additional steps before going out into the sun. Apply your daywear preparation, such as my SKIN PASTE, with your bronzing product *over* it for further protection.

You should protect your neck with a pretty scarf. This area is the first to show age—dryness, the prelude to wrinkling—and must always be shielded from the sun.

After your *short* sunbath, cleanse your face thoroughly, following the total routine, and apply a nourishing cream for ten minutes as an added softening measure.

At every age, you should protect your eye area, including your eyelids if they tend to be dry, by applying your daywear preparation under your bronzing product. Use sunglasses to keep from squinting; you may remove them for a few minutes at a time to avoid white circles.

The sides of your mouth and the outer corners of your eyes are most prone to expression lines. Put an extra dab of the proper sun preparation on these areas and reapply as needed. These areas have no surface oil to replenish the loss from sun exposure and must be protected by you.

If your skin feels very uncomfortable after exposure, follow the MILK BATH and the OIL COMPRESS treatments (described in chapter 7, "Approaching the Vintage Years") daily and limit your time in the sun.

Those with —3 and —4 skin should seriously consider shielding their face with an attractive wide-brimmed hat which can be both flattering and protective.

I understand that the image of a deep, dark brown look is both sensual and luxurious, but you needn't depend on the sun for it. I have found that by using deepening shades of my daywear preparation, I can develop a gradual, believable look without suffering the drying effects of the sun.

I work with four different shades, starting with my everyday one. After my first day in the sun, I begin to use one a little darker, but in the same family. After the second day, I use the third color and so on, until my tan is just as I like it—and no one except me knows where the beautiful glow came from!

You needn't hide from the sun: you can enjoy it with just a little caution.

At home during the summer months, *air conditioning* becomes your next foe. Air conditioning might be a luxury to many, but it can rob the air of the moisture your skin needs.

Use it wisely, only when necessary, and try to keep your thermostat set at 65 to 68 degrees for your skin's comfort. If your air-conditioner is in use, be sure that your skin is protected, not bare. Apply a light veil of a mineral oil complex, blotted, with or without the additional application of your day-wear preparation.

SUN SENSE
FOR THE PLUS SKIN

Those with PLUS skin are fortunate enough to be able to acquire an attractive tan without damaging your complexion *if* you take the necessary precautions. An oily skin has more than enough oil to withstand a loss from the drying effects of the sun. But too much exposure can harm your skin, leaving the scarf cuticle parched, trapping the lubricating oils beneath it. You can enjoy the sun, but build up a tan gradually—you won't get a deep look *and* preserve your soft skin if you try to get it all in a day. The result of such careless exposure is usually sunburn, a painful scorching of the skin that no one enjoys.

In moderation, the sun can not only give you a pretty tan, it can also draw some of your excess oils to the surface —but, remember, you don't want to dry out your surface skin.

Carefully start with just a half hour to three quarters of an hour, but never during the strong hours of noon to three. Your complexion needs time to adapt to the change. Gradually build up your pigment tone and you will be able to withstand the sun for longer periods.

Those who "tan naturally," without the help of any preparations, will still want to begin sunbathing in small doses.

Those who usually "burn first" will benefit from a greaseless sun product in liquid form—never a cream or oil for you! You want a preparation that includes an effective sunscreen, as does my preparation SUN LOTION. Don't neglect your nose, which usually has a tendency to burn.

The area around your eyes, your upper lip area, and your neck will need additional protection, as these areas tend to be dry. Sunglasses will help you keep from squinting, as will a wide-brimmed hat, especially helpful if you are outdoors but have had enough sun.

As you mature into your thirties and onward, you will want to apply your daywear preparation, such as SKIN PASTE, to these areas before you apply the greaseless sun product.

Your neck will stay protected if you wear a scarf tied around it. This area is the first to show age and I know you'll want to postpone that for as long as you can.

Don't neglect your chest, a part of your body particularly sensitive to the sun and sunburning. Use your greaseless product to block out harmful rays reaching this skin. Use an oil based bronzing product on the dry areas of the body to supplement the loss of oil and bring out a tan.

At home, air conditioning should be used as needed to keep you comfortable. This will control perspiration, which can aggravate an oily skin condition.

Because the sun-like rays are beneficial to the PLUS skin, you might like to buy a sun lamp for use after the summer months. I suggest a pure quartz lamp which, although more expensive than the others, gives far more noticeable results. Thirty to sixty seconds taken at the same time every day is all you'll need. Be sure to follow in-dividual directions concerning the distance at which to keep the lamp—usually twelve to eighteen inches from your face, and protect your eyes with cotton pads or sunglasses. Best results are achieved by turning to the right, then to the left after full-face exposure.

ADVICE FOR THE ATHLETIC WOMAN

For the PLUS *complexion:*

In the COMBINATION skin section of chapter 5, "Problem Skin: Breakthrough or Breakout," I explained what can happen to the person with *oily* skin who takes prolonged exposure to the sun and the elements without taking the necessary steps to protect her complexion. If, through jogging, playing tennis or golf, swimming, or partaking in any of the outdoor sports, you developed this condition of a parched scarf cuticle, you will have already read about it and have begun to correct it.

To prevent the COMBINATION skin condition from returning, you will want to take the sun cautiously and, when you are preparing for your exercise, you will apply your daywear preparation and additionally will use

your greaseless sun preparation over it. (Using my COLORED ASTRINGENT beneath SUN LOTION will help control the increased perspiration, which results from your activity, as it frees your pores of excess oil.)

If your exercise is indoors, a calisthenics or a dance class, for example, you will still want to have your daywear preparation in place to control oiliness and perspiration.

After exercising, I want you to thoroughly follow your morning routine for cleansing in addition to your shower, to cleanse your skin of the additional perspiration and grime.

Remember that caring for your face is as important as exercising your body —don't neglect either.

For the MINUS *complexion:*

The athletic woman with dry skin will need to take the necessary precautions against further dryness.

When exercising outdoors, in the sun, wear a greaseless sun preparation instead of the bronzing oil for a more comfortable feeling as you play tennis or golf or whatever your preference. This product is used over your daywear preparation as an additional shield to keep your complexion soft and pliant. Always follow your exercise routine with your skin care program—you should never neglect one part of your body for the other.

Everyone should remember to use a lip salve such as my LIP SARTINIZER when outdoors to prevent drying and chapping, in summer and winter alike.

ENDING
WINTER WORRIES

Winter is synonymous with dryness and dryness must be prevented by all means. Winter affects the MINUS skin more readily than the PLUS skin, which has enough oil to stay supple through even the cold and wind. Therefore *those with dry skin* will want to give their complexion extra care and attention.

This is accomplished by never leaving your home without your daywear preparation on your face. When you return home, if your MINUS face has been assaulted by wind and the chapping cold, cleanse thoroughly and give your complexion a light nourishing cream treatment for ten minutes. You may also follow with the OIL COMPRESS described in chapter 7.

You needn't be afraid of bathing, if you use your rich, fatty acid based soap. Follow your bath with a well-formulated body lotion, paying special attention to your elbows and knees, your hands and your feet. Additionally, you may wish to use your hand cream on these areas if they are exceptionally dry. Now is a good time to reapply your lip salve as well.

Those with PLUS *skin* who notice winter body dryness can follow these suggestions as well, omitting any areas prone to breaking out, such as the chest and back.

Winter's use of steam or thermal heat can be harmful to dry skin, dehydrating it. Used in excess, this can affect the oily skin as well, causing increased perspiration, which can aggravate it.

Keep your home at a comfortable 65 to 68 degrees and, for those with MINUS skin, use a room humidifier to put moisture back in the air.

If you have dry skin and are staying indoors, you will keep a light veil of your mineral oil complex, blotted, on your face to make it comfortable.

If you have oily skin, you will use your WHITE ASTRINGENT or daywear preparation to control the flow of oil.

When going outdoors, everyone will want to protect their neck and throat by wearing a scarf. If the temperature falls below thirty-two degrees, I strongly suggest using your scarf as a veil to shield your entire face. When you reach your destination, you can simply remove it without the fear of taut or chapped skin, whether you have a MINUS or a PLUS complexion.

Winter needn't be a worry if you take care.

STRESS SIGNALS

Stress ages a MINUS skin because the expression lines that reflect it can easily deepen due to the lack of skin pliancy.

The PLUS skin is affected somewhat differently; stress causes a rise in the milk-like substance of our blood, called lactate, leaving the skin more susceptible to blemishes.

We all know what being under pressure can mean, but did you realize that

even a happy stress—a laugh or a smile—can create a wrinkle?

I wouldn't think to suggest that you stop smiling—that is one of our greatest expressions. But you can smile more comfortably if you know that your face is protected by a preparation that is helping restore your skin's elasticity.

If you have MINUS skin, you will use your emollient daywear preparation to achieve this.

If you have PLUS skin, you will use this preparation around the eye area, on your upper lip area, and your neck, as these are usually dry and subject to increased wrinkling; of course, you'll wear your water-and-alcohol based preparation on the oily areas.

If you're a person who doesn't have a light, happy nature, it's about time you started cultivating one! The expression lines that are caused by a sullen disposition may stay with you long after your disposition has mellowed. And that might make you discontented all over again.

How to change your personality? Well, I don't suggest that you run to a monk's retreat for your spiritual uplifting, but you should think about meditating to clear your mind of all negative influences. Be your own guru.

Concentrate on organizing your mind for a happier, less hectic life. My life involves running a skin care institute, organizing a large staff, and coping with a long workday. Yet I have learned to stay tranquil by being in full control of my thoughts, even when there is the confusion of others swirling around me.

I believe in the saying "Make haste slowly." Keep your calm even when those around you seem to be losing theirs.

Now I'm not saying that there aren't times when this seems close to being impossible, but it's just at these moments that calm should prevail.

Learn to bend like a bough in the wind and your spirit will never be broken.

It is important to live with a feeling of tranquility. Keep your mind open to challenges so that you may enjoy life to the fullest. And the more tranquil we are, the clearer our outlook, and our complexion.

Cosmetic Surgery: Promiscuous or Prescribed?

Cosmetic surgery does not always accomplish the miracles we have been led to believe it does. It could possibly help you recapture your lost youth; it may rekindle passion in the heart of a spouse or a lover. It can remedy or at least improve certain facial flaws and, in the hands of today's highly skilled surgeons, can be performed with hardly a trace to show for it. But it is above all a surgical technique and must, like all medical services, be bought discriminately. Plastic surgery may not be a cure-all and it is surely not for everyone.

Cosmetic surgery can be the answer for a person who lives in the public eye and for whom facial appeal is a necessity for continued success. It can bring new hope to the mature widow who lived only for her husband and now, depressed by the signs of age on her face, is frightened by the thought of building a new life of her own. If a man feels that his facial flaws are keeping him from getting a better job, plastic surgery might be the boon he needs.

All of these examples involve extenuating circumstances that give validity to the choice of having this special surgery performed. In addition, there must be an actual problem to solve. If you feel terribly self-conscious about the size of your nose, if it truly inhibits you; if your eyelids droop heavily, presenting a health as well as a beauty problem; if a poor bone structure has caused your face to hang in folds; if you have a "turkey gobbler" neck; if you suffer with a disfiguring scar or demarcation; or if you have a genetic condition, such as prominent bags under your eyes, then you have a true and concrete reason to elect to have the surgery which your doctor will most likely agree to prescribe.

What I cannot condone is the promiscuous or baseless surgery that is the first recourse of many who discover their first wrinkle or crevice. Surgery performed before it is needed will only have to be repeated over and over again.

I think it's wonderful that we place a strong emphasis on maintaining a youthful appearance, but that doesn't mean we can all look twenty years old forever. You can have the allure of a man or a woman who has experienced life and still remain youthfully appealing, without the help of cosmetic surgery.

If your skin should lack luster or elasticity, you must help it restore these qualities through your skin care program—the plastic surgeon won't accomplish this goal for you.

There are three techniques, commonly used, that are aimed at restoring the skin's smooth texture. I would like to offer you my opinions on *dermabrasion, chemosurgery,* and the use of *silicone.*

Dermabrasion, a scraping of the skin's top layers, and chemosurgery, a peeling of the skin layers through the use of an acid based formula, have been frequently used to reduce acne scarring and pitting. Two requirements have to be met before you decide on either technique. *One:* any acne condition must be cleared beforehand. If not, the technique is useless; your complexion will revert to its former condition, necessitating repeated visits. *Two:* you must determine for yourself whether or not the actual condition of your skin is such that it interferes with your life and your well-being.

Undertaken after these two requirements have been satisfied, dermabrasion and chemosurgery can lessen acne scarring if the scars are not too deeply pitted. Still, you should never rush into either of these procedures unless it is an absolute necessity, as there are risks involved (and these should be discussed with your doctor).

I am even less in favor of the silicone injections being used to "plump" wrinkles and frown lines in the hope of diminishing them. Silicone, although accepted by the body, travels. Until we can find a substance that, injected with it, will hold it stationary, it would be wise to forget about this procedure.

I must caution you again to be certain of any decision you make. When you think you are sure that surgery is the answer for you, think it through once more. Be sure that your problem is a physical one, and that it is not mental: surgery shouldn't be used as a means of cheering yourself up, of getting a little lift, nor should it be undertaken because you think it might be fun and novel.

If you are unsure, begin, the proper skin care routine and watch your complexion respond. By keeping a PLUS skin free of excess oils and by keeping a MINUS skin comfortable and pliant,

you will reduce the chance of wrinkling and the need for a drastic solution to that problem.

If you think that you could use the benefits of cosmetic surgery, but are afraid of taking the risks involved, why not consider the makeup alternative of *camouflage?*

CAMOUFLAGING YOUR FLAWS

Camouflaging or shadowing your flaws is easily accomplished by using two shades of your daywear preparation (one darker than the other), a brown and a toast shade of shadow, as needed.

To lessen the appearance of sagging jowls: after applying the proper daywear preparation to your face as indicated in chapter 4, "Making Makeup Work for You," use a deeper shade of your daywear product or the brown shadow on the area under the jawline. Blend the edges well to avoid a noticeable line of demarcation. The darker color will cause the area to recede.

To thin a wide nose: apply your

daywear preparation to the nose area. Lightly apply the darker color to both sides of the nose, blending the edges well. This will cause the sides to recede, giving your nose a more narrow appearance.

To shorten a long nose: apply a touch of rouge or brown colored shadow just under the tip after applying your daywear preparation.

To hide puffiness under the eyes: after applying your daywear preparation and face powder, you can use a light toast eye shadow to lessen the appearance of puffiness. Looking into your mirror sideways, apply the shadow just over the bottom of the swelling to disguise the bulge.

Experiment with your two shades of daywear preparation, the brown and toast shadows, and your rouge to highlight your good features and minimize the flaws, though these can, at times, be interesting. Then, if you still feel your needs require more drastic measures, begin considering cosmetic surgery—but not a moment before!

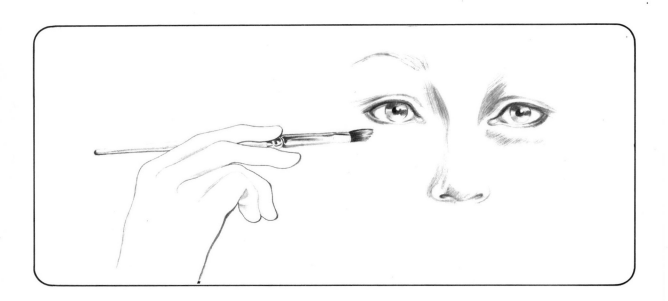

12

My Most Frequently Asked (and Answered) Questions

1. Why are my pores continually clogged—I wash my face often?

This is the question I hear most from my first-time clients with oily skin. I try to explain, during the initial visit, why washing alone cannot correct this condition.

When overly active sebaceous glands produce more oil than your pores can excrete, or when pores cannot discharge the oils rapidly enough, they collect in the pore passage where they harden and lodge. *Using only soap and water cannot dislodge the clogs or clear passages.*

I begin by putting my clients on my corrective program; the use of specially formulated astringents helps dislodge the clogs by causing them to become more fluid, thus enabling the excess oils to be released and the skin to regain its elasticity.

2. What is a whitehead? What is a blackhead?

First let me say that a blackhead is not in any way related to a whitehead. The blackhead is a hardening of excess oils in the pore passage and opening. As it lodges in the passage, it may oxydize, turning the tip dark or black. The clog is still a blackhead even if it does not oxydize.

A whitehead is formed on a dry skin by dead skin cells that have not sloughed off. These lodge under the skin surface, forming a keratin deposit. The pore openings are covered over. On removal, the substance is round and shiny, almost pearl-like.

There is a condition that forms in the under-eye area that looks like a whitehead, but is not. This is characterized by tiny white pinpoints that lie under the skin surface and can be either fatty deposits or granular embedments. These can be drawn to the surface and discharged through the use of my astringents. This condition and the blackhead condition primarily affect the PLUS skin; whiteheads affect MINUS skin. This is one key to distinguishing between them.

3. My skin feels dry. Does that mean I need a moisturizer?

If you have a MINUS skin, be it a —1, a —2, a —3, or a —4, you will need additional moisture or lubrication, but that doesn't mean you should use a heavy moisturizer.

The combined use of a light nourishing cream and an emollient based daywear preparation is so effective that you will probably not need any other products, certainly not a greasy formulation that, in the end, won't benefit or enhance your skin.

4. My skin is oily. Should I use a moisturizer?

No. Many ill-advised "experts" writing on beauty today will tell you that using a moisturizer "seals in water." What they don't tell you is that this product contains emollients or oil based ingredients which can make an oily skin oilier and aggravate a clogged pore condition. You want to *normalize,* not moisturize.

5. How can I keep from showing my age—I've already begun to notice a slackening of my skin's elasticity?

There is nothing so precious to us as maintaining a youthful appearance, and nothing more devastating than seeing those first signs of age.

If your skin is losing its elasticity, the reason might be poor skin care. Begin following the routine outlined in the chapter geared to your skin's individual needs. If you have a PLUS, or oily, skin, you can increase elasticity by keeping it free of excess oils. If you have MINUS, or dry, skin, keeping it soft and supple will accomplish this goal.

6. How can I prevent wrinkling under my eyes?

The skin around the eye is fragile and tends to be dry. The sebaceous glands are not secreting enough oil to keep it soft and pliant, able to release expression lines made when you smile or laugh, for example. These lines can deepen and become permanent.

The answer then is to increase the amount of lubrication in these areas through the use of emollient based preparations. They will be cleansed with a lubricating mineral oil complex and nourished throughout the day with an emollient based daywear preparation such as my SKIN PASTE. The

emollients work to increase the skin's suppleness, enabling it to release the expression or "laugh lines."

Using these products at an early age can prevent the lines from forming. Using them after the lines are present will help reduce them and prevent future ones.

7. I have dark circles under my eyes that don't go away though I've been getting enough sleep. Why is this so and what can I do about it?

Dark circles aren't always due to a poor night's sleep. This condition can be a natural discoloration due to veins that lie close to the skin surface. These won't disappear, but they can be camouflaged.

I don't recommend a cover-up product which would lie heavily on this delicate skin. Rather, depend on a lighter tint of your emollient based daywear preparation which will minimize the discoloration as it acts as a buffer against wrinkling and a shield against exposure. Starting at the inner corner, apply the product in the half-circle-shaped area under each eye.

Usually, a light flesh tone shade

works well. However, if the surrounding skin is ruddy, try a rosy hue to compensate without making it stand out.

And remember, you don't want a masking product; you want a preparation that does the job of lubricating as it camouflages.

8. What can I do to relieve puffiness under my eyes?

Puffy eyes will benefit from a simple treatment you can prepare. Steep a teabag in a cup of boiling water. When the liquid has cooled, use it to saturate two cotton pads. Place a pad over each closed eyelid and rest for three to five minutes. This will soothe the skin and reduce the swelling.

9. I have found that my acne pustules are reinfecting themselves—I need the help of a dermatologist, but how should I choose one?

Ask your family physician for his opinion and recommendation. Or consult a physician's directory that lists *recognized* doctors.

10. The skin of my body feels so dry I'm afraid to bathe. What can I do to soften it?

You can turn your bath into a softening treatment by adding bath oil to the water and using a fatty acid based soap. Enjoy the relaxing benefits of the bath as the enriched water soothes your dry skin. Afterward, apply a rich body lotion to further the softening effects of the soak and you need never be afraid of your tub again!

11. I love wearing wool sweaters, but I find that I develop an itchy rash from them. Is there a solution short of giving them away?

You can either have your sweaters lined with silk or cotton or wear a shirt of either fabric under the sweater to keep the wool from touching your skin. Cotton and silk are preferable materials as they offer the best barrier, protecting you from this sensitivity.

12. I just developed a rash around my mouth. What could it be caused by?

This particular type of irritation can affect just about anyone. Be suspicious of everything you have recently ingested, particularly foods that do not usually form part of your diet and foods or capsules with added minerals. If you have just switched to a new brand of toothpaste, suspect that. Go back to your old brand or try a milder dentifrice.

Depend on my well-shaken WHITE ASTRINGENT to remove any inflammation and promote healing.

13. Is there a remedy for a broken capillary—and the red blotch it leaves?

If a capillary or blood vessel lies close to the skin surface and is fragile, it can burst into a spidery red diffusion. To have the capillary removed medically is a painful procedure which may or may not work. Camouflaging with makeup will hide this condition effectively and painlessly.

After applying your daywear preparation and face powder, simply dust the reddened area lightly with an off-white or light toast colored shadow, using a narrow brush.

I would also like to caution you against certain practices which put pressure on the blood vessels and increase the possibility of broken capillaries. These are extremes of heat and cold, the drinking of full-bodied red wines, the use of slant-boards, and the standing on one's head.

14. What can be done about persistent brown spots on my hands and arms?

Pigment changes such as this, often called "age spots," are most perplexing because there is no solution for them —they have stumped the medical world for years! Bleaching them does not work as successfully as we would like nor do the numerous creams that claim to lighten them.

My advice would be to stop worrying about them—remember that they are far more noticeable to you than to anyone else. However, if you have pigment changes that are raised or change character in any way, consult your dermatologist.

15. How can my pregnancy affect the quality of my skin?

According to Dr. Ann C. Hill, the dermatologist I frequently call on when I see the need for medical advice for a client, major changes in the glandular system occur during pregnancy and are reflected in your complexion, usually during the first three months of the term.

Pregnancy can work both for and against the skin. In some cases, increased circulation will give a greater glow to your skin and hair. However, sometimes the greater increase in body fluids triggers additional oil secretions, making oily skin oilier. In this case, follow your PLUS skin program for a minimum of three times a day.

Women with MINUS skin who find their skin less soft and pliant than usual should increase their use of the emollient based products, the mineral oil complex, and the nourishing cream.

Additionally, you should avoid overexposure to the sun to prevent chloasma or masking, the deposit of dark pigment in small or large areas on the face. Certainly if you are prone to pigment changes, you should take special care to avoid the sun.

Higher hormonal levels resulting in a large discharge of estrogen can dilate the blood vessels and cause a spidery network of capillaries to appear. This usually disappears after pregnancy when the hormonal balance returns to normal. While the condition exists, you can camouflage this discoloration with an off-white shadow as discussed in question 13.

16. Should I use a "buf-puf" or other sloughing product?

No. The scarf cuticle or top layer of skin is a protective layer. Scrubbing or buffing can irritate your complexion or weaken the skin by robbing it of its healthy vitality. Dead skin cells are sloughed off naturally.

13.

Celebrity Complexions

I know how interested we all are in learning of the ways in which some of our most beautiful and well-known celebrities actually achieved their image of perfection.

If I were to list all of the names of the beautiful people I've cared for, there would not be enough pages in this book.

But let me tell you about just a few of the fabulous faces that fill our fashion and entertainment world.

I'd like to point out that this perfection is never accomplished through guesswork or a hit-and-miss program. That look we all admire, and sometimes envy, is achieved through dedi-cation and a willingness to discipline yourself, like an athlete.

I can truthfully say that **Princess Elizabeth of Yugoslavia** knew me when . . . Before we enlarged the Madison Avenue salon to its present size, when we had much smaller quarters, Elizabeth used to follow me into the laboratory and putter around! We developed a mutual admiration and have become very good friends.

I admire Elizabeth's down-to-earth naturalness and believe her to be a truly classic beauty. Elizabeth has good skin yet needs the proper preparations to bring out its best qualities.

When the Princess was married to

Howard Oxenberg and lived in New York, I was fortunate to be able to see her frequently. Now that she lives in Europe, we exchange letters and her preparations are sent to her in England. Whenever Elizabeth is in New York, she is sure to stop by for both a friendly and an official visit.

I started taking care of **Mary Martin** in the early 1960s, prior to her appearance in the Broadway show *Jennie*. The accumulative benefits of my work later enabled Mary to appear convincingly in the starring role of the seventeen-year-old bride in *I Do! I Do!*

Inez Robb, columnist in the then New York *Journal-American,* wrote an open letter to Miss Martin telling her that she was morally bound to share the secret of her youthful appearance—Miss Robb had almost decided not to see the show because she couldn't conceive of Miss Martin playing the part.

Miss Martin's reply was printed, mentioning that I was responsible, and my phone rang incessantly for several weeks!

I received credit for Mary Martin's makeup in the Playbill for both *Jennie*

and *I Do! I Do!* and will always treasure this memory.

When I first met **Gloria Vanderbilt** I was most impressed by her charming manner and great compassion. These qualities are reflected in everything Gloria does, especially her wonderful talent for fashioning colors and images.

Miss Vanderbilt has a distinctive sense of style in the highly individualized way that she dresses and wears her hair. Her fine, porcelain-like skin, complemented by her dark hair, is in perfect keeping with this great individuality. I love seeing Gloria's complexion flawless and free of the slightest temperamental reaction, of which I know it is all too capable.

When Gloria came to see me, I had questioned several minor irritations on her forehead. As she began using my preparations, she also wanted to finish a few of the products she had previously purchased. However, when the irritations did not disappear as quickly as I knew they should, I had to ask her to use my SKIN APPLICATION and WHITE ASTRINGENT, which I was certain would dissipate them rapidly—and they did.

Although Gloria's skin has a tendency to be temperamental, I keep it controlled beautifully with these preparations and her specially formulated daywear color, a lovely ivory shade with pink highlights. When Gloria told her close friend **Carol Matthau,** the wife of actor Walter Matthau, about this color, Mrs. Matthau admired it so much that we are now sending it to her in California.

Françoise de la Renta, one of the very special people I have had the privilege of caring for, is a most warm and giving woman. Because Mrs. de la Renta's life is so hectic, she comes to see me to release any buildup of tension and keep her face from showing fatigue from her busy schedule.

During the course of her visits, I have been able to bring her beautiful skin to its fullest potential. All of her friends comment on her special look, that luminous quality of her complexion. One of the effects I use to create this look is the coloring of her daywear preparation. I mix a beige shade with ash tones and then formulate two tints, a lighter one for the winter months, a deeper one for summer. Her complexion perfectly suits the glorious dark brown color of her eyes and hair.

Mrs. de la Renta feels, as I do, that as a woman matures, she is more appealing with a little flesh on her body, as sometimes being too thin can look scrawny.

Mrs. de la Renta unselfishly shares the secret of my work with her friends, which I appreciate, as there are many, as we all know, who would rather keep good things to themselves.

Babe Paley was by nature very striking in appearance. She was considered one of the most beautiful women of our time and was consistently listed as one of the ten best-dressed women of the world. However, at the time I met Mrs. Paley, I found that her skin care lacked that degree of perfection needed to complete this image.

There were areas that were being moisturized—again we come to that ill-advised practice—which should have been normalized with astringents. The tissues contained excess oils invisible to the untrained eye.

Mrs. Paley was certain that whatever she was doing was the right procedure for her skin. She was doubtful when I suggested that certain areas of her face required a different type of preparation than that which she was using.

During the course of our visits, when I proved to her the validity of my statements, she readily admitted that they were true and was very surprised that this had not been called to her attention previously.

I admired this quality in her to admit, yes, the Sartin system is better. Mrs. Paley was a person who, when she believed in someone, was most supportive.

Diana Vreeland is an outstanding example of what good taste and chic can mean in presenting an unforgettable portrait. In addition to being one of the kindest and friendliest of people, she is a most exciting woman. She is so witty and knowledgeable as well as being extremely talented. Putting it all together she becomes, in my mind, a vision of beauty and perfection.

Although Diana has a balanced complexion, her skin had lacked the luster and tone needed to give it the silky suppleness that would qualify it as superlative. This was accomplished through consistent application of the proper skin care program designed for her specific requirements.

Diana Vreeland can use makeup to make a strong statement: she uses a brilliant rose tint on her cheeks and emphasizes her eyes through her eye shadow and liner.

For those women who seek an example of the refinement of fashion and beauty, look to Diana Vreeland, the one who has contributed more than any other to perfecting the very essence of chic, by expressing her own individual style in the way she dresses, wears her maquillage, and coifs her hair. Mrs. Vreeland is not a conformer; she is a leader.

Joan Hackett is a very special person as well as a gifted actress. She has an inner light, an aura that you can feel, one that envelops you when you are near her. To me, Joan is like a precious jewel, a unique work of art, delicate, fragile, and rare.

Joan's skin is fine and translucent. I feel that I have been able to bring these qualities to the fullest potential.

Now that Joan has moved to California, we often discuss the possibility of my opening a salon on the West

Coast. Hopefully, this will be possible in the not-so-distant future. Until then, we will continue to send our preparations to Joan and all our California clients, from Beverly Hills to San Francisco.

Giorgio Sant' Angelo is one of my many male clients from the fashion world which include Calvin Klein and Halston.

What I like most about Giorgio is his sweet disposition and his spontaneity. At the same time, the impression given by his skin which, at our first visit, appeared to be of a heavy nature detracted from his outgoing personality. I felt then that his skin needed more tone and clarity.

One of my main interests, other than seeing the pores free of excess oil, was achieving a greater elasticity which had been lacking. My deep cleansing treatments and Giorgio's at-home use of the CLEAR and the WHITE ASTRINGENTS and the 1012 SOAP have brought a greater vitality to his skin.

I find Giorgio to be most honest in his thinking. As we spoke, he explained to me that he prefers to work only in areas that he is truly familiar with, putting his own talents to use on everything he puts his name to.

Baroness Marie-Hélène de Rothschild, who comes from a family of great repute and wealth, remains a very personable and active woman. I met the Baroness through the recommendation of Mrs. William Paley. On her short trips to the States, she must crowd many appointments and engagements into her busy schedule, yet includes visits to me for her skin care as well.

The Baroness has a well-balanced skin that complements her honey blond coloring. When she is not in New York, her preparations are shipped to Paris so that the Baroness can continue her at-home routine, which revolves around maintaining her lovely complexion.

I find taking care of the Baroness very stimulating and exciting, as she brings with her a flavor of that French mystique.

It has been very gratifying to watch those young girls I started on skin care early in life turn into elegant, talented women such as **Mica Ertegun, Chessy Raynor,** and **Nan Kempner,** among the many others.

Mica has a delicate, fragile beauty that can show fatigue very easily, particularly under her eyes. She uses SKIN PASTE to veil these areas.

Chessy has a heartier look, due in part to her excellent bone structure. She is especially fond of our LIP SARTINIZER, which she frequently orders.

I have tried to impress upon Nan, who loves being outdoors, that she must carefully protect her complexion with SKIN PASTE and a sunscreen, as her skin tends to be MINUS and cannot withstand this exposure.

Guarding against the sun is a lesson every woman should learn, yet it is only one aspect of the total skin care system which, begun at an early age, can keep you looking as youthful as these lovely ladies.

Bianca Jagger, one of my most recent devotees, has an exotic beauty. After having read and heard so much about Bianca, a woman very much in the limelight, I expected to find her distant and, perhaps, difficult. All to the contrary, Bianca is warm and responsive, eager to learn about and care for her skin.

Bianca was referred to me by her friend Halston. During her initial consultation, she told me that she had been using oils and moisturizers on her skin, which, upon examination, I found to have a tendency toward the PLUS side of the scale; she should never have been advised to use emollient based products.

With my encouragement and consistent care on Bianca's part, her skin will gain a glowing vitality.

When my secretary first told me that I had received a call from the **Duchess of Windsor,** for an appointment, I thought one of my friends was playing a joke on me!

It wasn't until the Duchess actually arrived at my salon that I realized the phone call was not a hoax. The Duchess had heard of me through her masseuse, at the time the late Dr. Laszlo, who was treating her, had broken his kneecap. Though he had suggested he would treat her from his wheelchair, she declined.

I found the Duchess of Windsor to be an elegant woman with compelling blue eyes. She wore a camellia in her lapel; it was always a part of her soignée, sophisticated look. The Duchess has an excellent bone structure, good cheekbones, and a strong jaw. In caring for her skin, one had to tread a very thin line between the fatty acids and the alkalines to achieve a pH balance.

What delighted me was the magazine reportage of the press conference the Duchess later gave. It described her as having wonderful skin and wearing very little makeup. Little did that reporter know the Duchess was wearing all my preparations!

There's no nonsense about **C. Z. Guest** and yet there is a great deal of warmth and friendliness about her. Mrs. Guest loves the outdoors and is a very ardent gardener. Because of this, her skin has been greatly exposed to the sun.

When I explained that overexposure is bad, as it dries out the skin and enables expression lines to remain, she readily understood and compared it to a plant which, when left in the sun for too long, similarly dries out and withers.

I am working to restore the lost moisture to her skin's outer layers, thus making it pliant enough to release expression lines. Mrs. Guest is both a very understanding and a very gracious lady.

I had been taking care of Clara La Roche—the Duchess, as Rosalind Russell loved to call her—for many years. One day I walked into my salon expecting to greet her. As I approached, I realized that the lady waiting for me was someone else and, in my surprise, exclaimed, "You're not Mrs. La Roche." To which the lady replied, "No, I'm taking my sister's place today. My name is **Rosalind Russell.**"

Miss Russell came to see me to maintain the good quality of her skin. Miss Russell had a tendency to become allergic; particularly subject were her eyelids. The program that I worked out for her alleviated this condition and helped achieve a normal balance.

I enjoy taking care of actresses and actors, as the challenge to prevent the deepening of lines due to facial expression used so frequently in the art of acting is ever-present, particularly in closeups.

I found Miss Russell to be a very vivacious person, full of life and spontaneity; we had a wonderful relationship. I best remember the day I introduced her to my then school-age son, Cary. Miss Russell spoke to him like a Dutch uncle, "Cary, my advice to you is to get on the school paper and that way you'll get to be very knowledgeable." She also told him that journalism was the career her own son had chosen. He is now assistant public administrator of the County of Los Angeles.

It is still hard for me to believe that this vibrant woman is no longer with us.

I was very thrilled when **Janet Gaynor** made an appointment to visit me many years ago. I remembered how much I enjoyed her portrayal of the heroine in *Seventh Heaven* with Charles Farrell. I also could not forget her wonderfully dewy look. When Miss Gaynor arrived and we were discussing her needs, her first words to me were—in that inimitable girlish voice—"Miss Sartin, I want you to give me the look I used to have." And I did.

To this day, Miss Gaynor continues using her special SKIN PASTE, tinted to a golden tan, sent to her in California along with the other preparations for her skin.

Janet Gaynor is a very giving, thoughtful person who was able to help me at a time when I was perturbed about my son Cary's going to camp for the first time. The possibility of accidents, especially as he hadn't yet learned to swim, seemed to trouble me the most. However, Miss Gaynor was able to set my mind completely at ease by her very simple yet profound philosophy. She said, "Miss Sartin, we must put our trust in God." That gave me pause and I found that I no longer felt as apprehensive. I will always think of Miss Gaynor with warmth and affection.

It was through Joan Hackett, whose translucent complexion I brought to its fullest potential, that I met **Carrie Fisher.** Because Joan felt that Carrie needed to begin a proper skin care program, she advised her to see me.

Since Carrie's skin has a tendency to secrete more than the desired amount of oil, it necessitates periodic visits to the salon for deep pore cleansing and a constant vigil at home with my CLEAR, WHITE, and COLORED ASTRINGENTS in addition to the 1012 SOAP.

Carrie is a dear and unassuming young person with a great sense of humor. She has a beautiful singing voice which she comes by honestly from her lovely mother, Debbie Reynolds, and her father, Eddie Fisher.

One of the greatest rewards in any kind of work that is constructive and beneficial is that it creates an unending chain as each succeeding person recommends my work to others. After becoming familiar with the results of my technique, Carrie recommended me to **Teri Garr,** another of my bright, young actresses.

Jill Clayburgh became aware of skin care at an early age, thanks to her mother, Julia Clayburgh, a client of whom I was most fond.

Although Jill knew of my work prior to her college days, she became seriously interested after discovering that her roommate at Sarah Lawrence College, Andrea Akers, was also a Janet Sartin devotee. Andrea had learned of me through her mother, Mrs. Anthony Akers, whose husband was our Ambassador to New Zealand.

Jill knew she had to be disciplined with her skin care, as her complexion has a tendency to tip to the PLUS side of the scale, which means that her pores can easily become blocked.

Therefore, she pays particular attention to her skin care.

Jill has always impressed me as being a very sweet, friendly, and sensitive person. She is also a most gracious hostess. I remember that lovely Christmas Eve party at her family's Manhattan townhouse. Although her mother had recently passed away, Jill was warm and attentive, making everyone feel so at home. It is pleasurable indeed to see that she has attained such a measure of success: she most certainly deserves it.

I first met **Barbara Sharma** in 1972 when she became concerned with preserving the youthful appearance of her skin. I was delighted to have the opportunity to meet her and care for her complexion because I had always been so impressed by her great vivaciousness in "Laugh-In." I enjoyed watching her and I especially remember her bright, lively tap numbers.

So often when you meet celebrities or performers, they aren't quite as energetic as they are on stage—they don't live up to their theatrical image, but Barbara certainly did. She gives you a feeling of youthful excitement, always ready to try something new, always doing something . . . and very concerned about doing the right things for her complexion. She has even called me, when traveling, if a particular question has come up. She is as dedicated and as consistent with her beauty care as she has been with her acting.

I have always thought of Barbara as being a completely honest person, practical in her evaluations. She was very receptive to the advice I gave her, very open-minded and willing to do what she could to keep that young, natural look. Willingness is one of the most important qualities you must have to achieve what you want, to actually apply yourself to the job. That's why Barbara is so talented as a performer and able to project great energy and insights into the characters she portrays—from the dancer on "Laugh-In" to the young wife in Broadway's *I Love My Wife*.

Lisa Pelikan is a rising young star. She is the versatile young actress who gave such a marvelous performance as the young *Julia* in that film. Lisa, who grew up in Rome and Japan, has a most appealing, natural, and charming disposition, although she can be stubborn and strong-willed on occasion.

Being of an aesthetic nature, Lisa wanted her complexion to be perfect. She also believes in looking to the future, to keep her skin youthful. Lisa's skin had too much of a good thing— and these oils weren't being properly distributed. I designed a daily program for her, one based on the use of my astringent products. Lisa also needed a different look that would be suitable for the camera. I developed a variation of COLORED ASTRINGENT so that she wouldn't have to wear any heavy, theatrical foundation to achieve the special coverage that the screen demands—a cosmetic most actresses have to put up with.

With my preparations, Lisa's skin has achieved a great clarity which emphasizes her delicate features and the bright color of her eyes.

Apart from acting, Lisa loves painting, writing, and reading. She enjoys relaxing and, at times, solitude. She is a thoroughly delightful girl and I look forward to helping her keep her good looks as she continues her very successful career.

Princess Ira Von Furstenberg is charming, elegant, and happy by nature. Her interests vary. She likes modern art as well as skiing. Her real love is decorating homes.

The Princess prefers to keep busy. She is presently doing public relations for Valentino, with a special interest in the designer's new perfume.

Princess Ira is a very stimulating and exciting person.

Laura Alvarez Cushing is a very beautiful, glamorous girl who has appeared on many magazine covers as well as on television, especially in her native Caracas. In Venezuela, she was a noted celebrity interviewer.

Laura is very creative in the design world and she often anticipates styles that will have a look for the future. She also loves riding and particularly favors the "jumpers."

Laura has had some trouble with her skin. In the time I have been her cosmetologist, her complexion has become increasingly clear and lovely.

Laura Cushing is a very serious person and, once her word has been given, you can depend on her to follow through.

Audrey Meadows (Mrs. Robert Six in private life), who spoke Mandarin Chinese before she spoke English, is one of the warmest and loveliest of people. Besides being fluent in many foreign languages, Miss Meadows loves reading, waterskiing, and tennis. Audrey likes to keep busy. One of her favorite hobbies is vegetable and flower gardening which, she claims, next to her "darling Miss Sartin," does the most for her.

Audrey's skin is lovely, with a great deal of natural warmth. Her visits are a bright ray of sunshine.

Mrs. Alfred (Betsy) Bloomingdale is foremost a devoted daughter, wife, and mother with three wonderful children who are a constant delight to her. Now that they are all grown, Mrs. Bloomingdale is able to pursue her new interests. Besides being fascinated with food and flowers, she is designing loungewear for Swirl, her "latest and most exciting accomplishment."

Mrs. Bloomingdale, who has lovely skin, keeps herself Sartinized and is herself a most exciting accomplishment.

Bonita Granville, in private life Mrs. Jack Wrather, began her film career at the age of seven. Her first motion picture was *Westward Passage* in which she appeared as the daughter of Ann Harding and Laurence Olivier. Mr. and Mrs. Wrather had three children, Molly, Linda, and Christopher, before Bonita resumed her career, this time on television, starring in "The U. S. Steel Hour," "Studio One," and "Playhouse 90."

In 1958, Mrs. Wrather became the associate producer of the "Lassie" television series and, several years later, was made its producer. She is active today in many civic, charity, and cultural activities.

Bonita has good skin which can be temperamental, but with proper care and by being mindful of the sun, she will always have a lovely complexion. Both Mr. and Mrs. Wrather are exceptionally fine, warm, and compassionate people.

Silvana Mangano is exquisite! She has the face of a madonna—and I say this without exaggeration. Silvana is as beautiful on the inside as she is on the outside. She has superlative skin and all I do is keep it that way—and I intend to do so forever.

Silvana, who is totally devoted to the Sartin program, makes it a ritual to visit me in the salon twice a year. An actress in her own right, she lives in California with her husband, film producer Dino de Laurentiis.

Silvana gifted me with a great surprise at the end of her last visit to New York. I walked into my reception room after a day of treatments and saw, to my amazement, the biggest and most beautiful lily bush I had ever seen, the gorgeous white lilies all in bloom. With it was a lovely note, written to me in Italian, so that Silvana could truly express her feelings to me. This is only one of the many ways in which Silvana has shown her kindness and thoughtfulness. She is truly a gracious lady.

14

The Sartin Touch: The Salon Treatment

The Sartin touch means taking an interest in you, as an individual, and in the health and beauty of your skin. I personally want to know that your skin is becoming the best it can be, whether that means maintaining its loveliness or clearing it of problems. The Sartin touch begins as you enter one of my analytical centers or my original Institute on Madison Avenue. At the centers, you are greeted in a very friendly, concerned manner by the manager and seated at one of our tables. At the Institute, I would meet with you myself—I do also make personal appearances at all my centers so that you never have to feel that you're just a number on a waiting list or that I'm just the name on a bottle.

If you're visiting one of the centers, you will next meet with a trained beauty consultant who has worked with me at the Institute. She will take your name and other important information and then your analysis will begin.

First, she will give your skin a preliminary examination through the lighted magnifying glass at each table. This will determine whether she will remove your makeup with oil (if it appears to be dry or normal) or astringent (if it appears to be oily). Your skin can be accurately analyzed only if it is free of all makeup and soil (during the consultation, my preparations and treatment maquillage will be applied, creating an immediate metamorphosis, and you needn't worry about going out with a "bare" face).

The consultant will now do a more thorough examination of your skin to judge the degree of dryness or oiliness, whether it is allergic or sensitive as well. She will look for blemishes, wrinkles—all the different possible indications of your particular skin type. With many blemished skins, the hair fuzz on the face and neck is often involved in the problem—she will look along the sides of your neck, under your chin, and along your jawline as well.

All this pertinent information is listed on the chart that bears your name. You will also be given a booklet, one of those I designed for each of the skin types (balanced, oily: $+1$, $+2$, $+3$, $+4$; dry: -1, -2, -3, -4, allergic/sensitive). The booklet describes the characteristics of your skin type as well as indications for its care,

just as you have found in this book. The booklet also gives diet hints—I am a firm believer in caring for the skin from the inside as well as the outside.

Once your skin type has been professionally determined, your daywear preparations will be chosen. The consultant is also trained in makeup application and will help you select shades that will best enhance your natural coloring. The correct medium of each cosmetic is selected to work for your skin, just as your cleansing preparations do. In addition to daywear preparations, there are lipsticks, eye shadows, liners and mascaras, eyebrow pencils and brushes for use with each, and face powder, as well as powdered and creme rouges. The Sartin look for daytime, one which emphasizes your natural beauty, is applied and taught to you so that you can follow it at home. This is an important lesson, too. (At night, your approach to makeup is different. You want more glamour and that's fine. But during the day, I believe in keeping it natural and my consultants can show you how.)

You may be surprised to find a man at one of the next tables, but for some time now men have become increasingly concerned with keeping their skin clean and young-looking too. And quite a few of my male clients wear daywear preparations to keep their skin in line, without it appearing noticeable (as many commercial "bronzers" are). Some men use SKIN PASTE under their eyes to discourage wrinkles.

If you decide to try the Sartin program, you will receive, along with your preparations, a new appointment some four weeks later. This is to recheck your skin and evaluate your progress. Perhaps your skin type needs a slight revision if it's improved already. Perhaps you need a reminder about following your diet (I can always tell if you've been eating foods you should avoid and so can my beauty experts). We work along with you, helping you cope with any skin problems that might arise, helping you achieve a glowing skin that brightens your entire personality. We are concerned with progressively improving the quality of your skin and, as I've told you before, every skin has this potential.

Turning an average skin into a superlative one has always been my goal.

I always knew that I would be the best in my field when I began, in the late 1940s, but I never thought that my work would become so widely known. I had no idea, when I started my first salon in New York, that in time I would become the world's most acclaimed skin care expert. I was working by myself in office space that afforded room for a small lab and just one treatment area. I would have appointments with my small group of clients during the day and work in the lab during the morning or evening hours, perfecting my preparations. Soon it was too small for my growing clientele. I took time out to have a baby and I knew that when I reopened the Institute it would have to be in a larger location. After my sixth-month "leave," I was able to rent space at my present Madison Avenue address. Again I started with a single treatment room, a waiting room, and a lab, but as other suites on the floor became available, my Institute expanded.

As I became better known for my work, more and more people asked to be taken care of. First there were two, then three treatment rooms and three assistants. Now I have four assistants, four treatment rooms, two secretaries, a large lab, and a shipping room that handles orders from clients who live all over the world.

Still the demand to be placed on my program and receive my skin care products grew (not everyone needs the deep cleansings or the restorative series). I couldn't possibly see all those who called, even if only for consultations, which I would do at the start or very end of my day. I had a waiting list of fifty to a hundred people and it was growing. I needed a special salon just for them! But it wasn't possible until my son, Cary, came into the business. Cary had grown right along with the company and, when he finished college, he decided that he would like to take over the "financial end" of it. He did learn about it from all angles, including the beauty part— he has observed in the treatment room and is meticulous. In the past few years, he has devoted himself to our expansion. He began by scouring New York City for the right location to open our first analytical center. When the space at 480 Park Avenue became available, we knew it was right for us.

I was very enthusiastic about the idea because I knew that my beauty consultants would be experts in the field of analysis—aside from being trained makeup artists, each studied with me in the treatment room and would become well versed in the art and science of skin care. My consultants are more knowledgeable than any girls working over the counter could be and that's why 480 Park Avenue was such a success; it was able to stand on its own feet. It gave us the impetus to forge ahead. Of course, we didn't have to look far for our next center. In fact, three were offered to us by major department stores in the city. We selected Bonwit Teller.

Bonwit's offered us a large space with a private entrance on Fifty-sixth Street and we built the kind of skin care center we wanted. I feel that we have had competition at the public level (no one has yet come close to matching the care offered at the Institute), but no one has equaled the quality of attention we offer. As soon as our tables were set up at Bonwit's, the more commercial skin care lines at department stores nearby began advertising their one-to-one approach. However, tables instead of a counter do not make much difference if you can't back it with the knowledge to make the system work. Other companies, with money spent on advertising rather than a personalized approach and hours of new research, just can't compete with our knowledge of skin care.

Our next center opened early in 1978 at Riverside Square, a most unique mall in New Jersey. We were invited to join the exclusive shops presented in a beautiful, modern shopping area. Because we have so many clients in New Jersey, we decided to try opening this center a little farther from home. Now we are expanding across the country and internationally.

As always, I will continue to visit the centers and meet with my clients—that's the approach I have always taken and will always take. I feel very strongly about maintaining the standards I have built my reputation on, even though we are making our system more readily available to you. I won't be commercial now any more than I would have been thirty years ago. Because I'm not dependent on an over-the-counter enterprise, I don't have to worry about percentages and mass market appeal—I also don't have to lure customers with gimmicks. I have built my success on my results, slowly, steadily. I'm not interested in selling a

bottle of astringent and forgetting about that customer. I want to be able to watch her progress and be available if she has questions or special problems.

I've developed my preparations over the past forty years and I've studied the results. I wouldn't be bringing them to you if I weren't sure of them. My name's on every item. Once you're on my program, you receive a membership card that enables you to purchase products at any center. Without it, you can only buy preparations not directly related to skin care, such as lipstick, hand cream, body lotion, sun preparations, or my perfume, Janet Sartin. Because I believe so strongly in using preparations designed for your skin type only, I won't offer my preparations to you unless your skin has been analyzed (at no charge, if you visit the analysis centers). I'd rather lose the sale of a bottle of my astringent than sell it to a woman who doesn't want to take the time to use it properly (in conjunction with my other products). That's a concept that department store officials weren't too familiar with, as you'll soon see.

The manager of my center at Bonwit Teller's called me one afternoon while I was working at the Institute— a million and one other things were going on there! She explained that one of the store's regular customers wanted to buy a bottle of COLORED ASTRINGENT. The customer explained that she was using another brand of products for skin care but liked the particular shades we were offering for daywear preparations. I had to tell her that we couldn't sell her a random preparation because we couldn't monitor her skin's program unless she fully committed herself to our system. If she mixed the products from two different lines, I explained, she wouldn't achieve the look she wanted or the one we wanted her to have.

The woman, whom I'll call Mrs. Brown, became quite persistent and complained to the floor manager. He then called me and told me that he had promised her the astringent. I explained my reasoning to him as well. He countered by telling me that the store had looked up Mrs. Brown's record of purchases and found her to be one of their very good customers. They wanted her to have her way. But I couldn't take responsibility for her skin or for my product if she weren't going to use it correctly.

The next phone call came from one of the top executives. He said that he couldn't understand why all this fuss was being made over "a bottle of astringent." I explained that I wasn't interested in selling that bottle if it's not going to work toward creating the beautiful complexion that I am famous for. It couldn't do that without Mrs. Brown's total dedication. I'd sooner lose the sale than risk having her return in a week or two, unsatisfied, even if it would be her own fault. I'll stand by my bottles of astringent and the promise of accumulative results, and I'll maintain these standards for you and all my clients and readers as we continue to expand. That's the Sartin touch.

Index

Abrasive cleaning pads, 31
Acid/alkaline (pH)
    balance, 12–13, 27
Acne, 1, 18, 95, 162
    cosmetic surgery for,
        154–55
Age spots, 164
Aging, 115–22, 160–61
    exposure to elements,
        116
    minus skin, 116, 118,
        119–20, 121, 161
    plus skin, 117, 161
    stress, 116
Air conditioning, 145–46,
    147

Akers, Andrea, 174
Akers, Mrs. Anthony, 174
Alcohol
    astringent content, 31
    drinking, 140
Alkalines, 12–13
Allergic skin, 5, 25, 104,
    138
    problems, 104–7
    rouge, 68
    sun sense, 143, 144
    tea bag treatment,
        103–4, 125
Antibiotics, 95, 107
Astringents, 31. *See also*
    Clear astringent;

Colored astringent;
    White astringent
Athletic woman
    with minus skin, 149
    with plus skin, 147–49

Balanced skin, 2, 12, 14,
    45
    cleansing preparations,
        32
    daywear preparations,
        52, 53, 78
    eye makeup removal,
        37–39
    lipstick removal, 37
    pH factor, 12–13, 27

rouge, 60, 68
skin care system, 39–41
Bath/bathing, 123, 134–36
Bath oil, 134, 163
Bath powder, 136
Beige daywear
preparations, 53
Beige face powder, 61
Blackheads, 15, 17, 18, 21,
22, 37, 80, 95,
159–60
Black skin, 97
Bleaching, facial hair, 130
Blemishes, 15, 16, 17, 18,
82
neck, 82
treatment for, 86–87
Bloomingdale, Betsy (Mrs.
Alfred), 176
Body exercises, 133
Body lotion, 134, 163
Body temperature, 12
Boils, 15, 16, 18, 82, 92
Bone structure, 116
Bonwit Teller, 181,
182–83
Brisson, Freddie, 45
Bronzing oil, 144
Bubble bath, 134
Buffers, 31, 165

Camouflage, 155–58
for circles under eyes,
161–62
for nose, 155–58

Capillaries, broken,
163–64, 165
Celebrity complexions,
166–77
Checklists
cleansing preparations
and tools, 45
makeup preparations
and tools, 78
Chemosurgery, 154–55
Chin, 22–24, 29
Clayburgh, Jill, 174
Clayburgh, Julia, 174
Cleansing, 5, 6, 26, 29,
31–32
basic tools, 35
nighttime, 37, 114
preparations and tools
checklist, 45
Cleansing oil, 32, 36, 37,
39, 52, 56, 84, 93, 98,
101, 106, 119, 120,
122
Cleansing preparations, 2,
29–34
balanced and minus skin,
32
plus skin, 31–32
Clear astringent, 31, 40,
83, 88, 93, 99, 101,
106, 120, 130, 134,
170, 173
Cold, protection against,
149–50
Collagen (protein) cream,
119

Colored astringent, 52, 53,
60, 84, 85, 86, 94, 99,
102, 106, 173, 175,
183
Color selection
daywear preparations, 53
eye shadow, 64
face powder, 61
rouge, 68
Combination skin
problems, 97–100
Complexion, 9. See also
Minus skin; Plus skin
Compresses
oil, 122, 124, 149
white astringent, 89–92,
124
Congested pores, 15, 16,
21, 37, 82, 159
superficial, 80
systemic, 80
Consistency, 5, 6, 41–42
Correction, 2, 5, 6, 29
Cosmetic surgery, 153–55
chemosurgery, 154–55
dermabrasion, 154–55
silicone injections, 154,
155
Cotton, sterilized, 35, 78
Cotton swabs, 45, 78
Creams
collagen (protein), 119
heavy night, 121
superfatted, 32, 36, 40,
85, 94, 100, 103, 107,
120, 121

Cushing, Laura Alvarez, 176
Cyst, 92

Daywear preparations, 47–60, 78
  application, 53
  astringent based, 52
  balanced skin, 52, 53
  camouflage with, 155–58
  color selection, 53
  emollient, 52, 80
  minus skin, 47, 52, 53, 78
  plus skin, 47, 52, 53, 78
  tanned look with, 145
Dead skin cells, 12, 31, 165
De la Renta, Françoise, 168
Deodorants, 136
Depilatories, 129–30
Dermabrasion, 154–55
Dermatologists, 95
  choosing, 162
Dermis, 12
Dieting, 140
Dryness
  rating degrees of, 20–22
  young complexion problem, 110–12
Dry skin, 5, 12, 14
  bathing, 163
  increasing elasticity, 161
  winter care, 149–50
  See also Minus skin

Eisenhower, Mamie, 126
Elasticity
  increasing, 161
  loss of, 15, 80
Electrolysis, 129, 130, 132
Elizabeth, Princess of Yugoslavia (Mrs. Howard Oxenberg), 166–67
Emollient daywear preparations, 52, 80
Enzymes, 140
Epidermis, 12
Ertegun, Mica, 170, 171
Exercising, 132–33
Exfoliating preparations, 31
Exposure to elements, effect of on skin, 20, 116, 142
Eyebrow contouring, 67, 130
Eyebrow pencil, 64, 67, 78
Eyelashes, 67
  false, 68
Eye liner, 67, 78
Eye makeup, 63–68
  application, 64–67
  color selection, 64
  cream, 64, 67
  eyebrow contouring, 67, 130
  false eyelashes, 68
  liner, 67
  mascara, 67–68

pencil, 64, 67, 78
powder, 63, 67
removal, 37–39
Eyes
  dark circles under, 56, 60, 161–62
  pinpoint deposits under, 81
  puffiness under, 158, 162
  wrinkling around, 19, 161
Eye shadow, 78
  cream, 64, 67
  pencil, 64, 67, 78
  powder, 63, 67

Face masks, 124–25
  mud, 125
Face powder, 60–63
  application, 63
  color selection, 61
  loose form, 60, 61, 78
  pressed (compact) form, 60–61
Facial exercises, 132–33
Facial hair, 129–30
Facials, 2, 123–24
Fair skin, 143
False eyelashes, 68
Farrell, Charles, 173
Fatty acids, 12–13
Fisher, Carrie, 173–74
Fisher, Eddie, 174
Forehead
  in T-zone, 22–24, 29
  wrinkling, 19

Foundation, makeup, 2, 46, 47. *See also* Daywear preparations

Garr, Terri, 174
Gaynor, Janet, 173
Granville, Bonita (Mrs. Jack Wrather), 176–77
Gravity, effect of on skin, 115–16
Guest, C. Z., 172

Hackett, Joan, 169–70, 173
Hair, 42
    body, 132
    facial, 82, 88, 129–30
    hot oil treatment, 126
Hair spray, 42
Halston, 170, 171
Hand cream, 134
Harding, Ann, 177
Heavy night cream, 100, 121
Hepburn, Katharine, 69
Hill, Ann C., 164
Honey-tinted daywear preparations, 53
Hot oil hair treatment, 126

I Do! I Do! (play), 167
I Love My Wife (play), 175

Jagger, Bianca, 171

Jawline, 42, 82, 87
Jennie (play), 167
Julia (movie), 175

Kempner, Nan, 170
Klein, Calvin, 170

Lama, Gemma, 132
La Roche, Clara, 172
"Lassie" (TV series), 177
Laszlo, Erno, 1
"Laugh-In" (TV series), 174, 175
Lip Sartinizer, 63, 72, 126, 171
Lipstick, 72, 78
    removal, 37–39

Makeup, 1, 2, 46–78
    daywear preparations, 47–60
    eye, 63–68
    face powder, 60–63
    lighting and checking, 76
    lipstick, 72–75
    preparations and tools checklist, 78
    rouge, 60, 68–69
    young complexion, 112–14
    See also separate listings
Makeup base, 2, 46, 47. *See also* Daywear preparations
Makeup mirror, 76, 78
Male clients, 170, 180

Mangano, Silvana (Mrs. Dino de Laurentiis), 177
Martin, Mary, 167
Mascara, 67, 78
Masks, 124–25
    mud, 125
Matthau, Carol (Mrs. Walter), 168
Meadows, Audrey (Mrs. Robert Six), 176
Milk bath, 121–22, 125
Minus (—) skin, 14, 19–22, 45
    aging, 116, 118, 119–20, 121, 161
    athletic woman, 149
    cleansing preparations, 32
    daywear preparations, 47, 52, 53, 78
    dryness, young complexion, 110–12
    exposure to elements, 20
    eye makeup removal, 37–39
    increasing elasticity, 161
    lipstick removal, 37
    milk bath, 121–22, 125
    —1, 20–21
    —2, 21
    —3, 21; aging, 116, 118, 119–20, 121, 161
    —4, 22; aging, 116, 118, 119–20, 121, 161

oil compress, 122, 124, 149

rating degrees of dryness, 20–22

rouge, 60, 68

skin care system, 39–41

and stress, 150, 152

sunburn, 20

sun sense, 143, 144–46

whiteheads, 159–60

winter care, 149–50

wrinkles, 22, 117

Moisturizers, 3, 80, 160

Mouth

rash, 163

wrinkling at corners, 19

Mud mask, 125

Neck blemishes, 82

New York *Journal American,* 167

Nose

blackheads, 17, 21, 22

camouflage for, 155–58

oiliness, 21, 22, 29, 31, 82

Nutrition, 138–40

Oil compress, 122, 124, 149

Oiliness

nose, 21, 22, 29, 82

rating degrees of, 16

young complexion problem, 108–10

Oily skin, 5, 12, 13, 14

elasticity loss, 80

foods to be avoided, 139

winter care, 150

See also Plus skin

Olive-toned skin, 144

Olivier, Laurence, 177

Pale skin

daywear preparations, 53

face powder color, 61

Paley, Babe (Mrs. William), 168–69

Pedicure, 136

Peeling preparations, 31

Pelikan, Lisa, 175

pH factor, 12–13, 27

Pink face powder, 61

Pink-tinted daywear preparations, 53

Plastic surgery. *See* Cosmetic surgery

"Playhouse 90" (TV series), 177

Plus (+) skin, 13, 15–19, 45

aging, 117

athletic woman, 147–49

blackheads, 160

cleansing preparations, 31–32

congested pores, 80, 159

daywear preparations, 47, 52, 53, 78

eye makeup removal, 37–39

foods to be avoided, 139

increasing elasticity, 161

lipstick removal, 37

moisturizers, 80, 160

mud mask, 125

oiliness, young complexion, 108–10

+1, 17, 82

+2, 17, 82

+3, 17–18, 82–85, 89

+4, 18–19, 89, 92–97

rating degrees of oiliness, 16

rouge, 68

skin care system, 35–36

and stress, 150, 152

sun sense, 143, 146–47

winter care, 150

wrinkles, 117

Pregnancy, and skin quality, 164–65

Prevention, 7, 115

Problem skins, 79–107

allergic skin, 104–7

combination skin, 97–100

plus skin, 80–97

sensitive skin, 101–3

Protection, 7, 115

Pustules, 15, 16, 18, 82, 92

Rash

around mouth, 163

wool-induced, 163

Raynor, Chessy, 170, 171

Reynolds, Debbie, 174

Riverside Square Center, 182
Robb, Inez, 167
Rosewater, 125–26
Rothschild, Marie-Hélène de, 170
Rouge, 68–69, 78
  allergic skin, 68
  application, 69
  balanced skin, 60, 68
  color selection, 68
  cream, 60, 68, 69
  minus skin, 60, 68
  plus skin, 68
  powdered, 68, 69
  sensitive skin, 68
Ruddy (reddish) skin
  daywear preparations, 53
  face powder color, 61
Russell, Rosalind, 45, 172–73

Sallow skin
  daywear preparations, 53
  face powder color, 61
Sant' Angelo, Giorgio, 170
Sartin, Cary, 126, 172–73, 181
Sartin salon treatment, 2, 178–83
Scarf cuticle, 12, 165
Sebaceous (oil) glands, 12, 15, 80
Sensitive skin, 5, 25, 138
  problems, 101–3
  rouge, 68

sun sense, 143, 144
tea bag treatment, 103–4, 125
Seventh Heaven (movie), 173
Sharma, Barbara, 174–75
Shaving
  teenage boys, 87–88
  unwanted facial hair, 129, 132
Silicone injection, 154, 155
Skin application, 85, 86, 87, 89, 92, 93, 94, 97, 100, 134, 167
Skin care system, 5–8, 26–45
  balanced and minus skin, 39–41
  plus skin, 35–36
  See also Problem skins
Skin cells, dead, 12, 31, 165
Skin paste, 52, 53, 56, 84, 86, 94, 99, 102, 107, 171, 180
Skin quality analysis, 9–10
Skin scale, 13–14
Skin types, 9–25
  allergic, 25
  balanced, 14
  combination, 24
  minus (−), 14, 19–22
  plus (+), 14, 15–19
  sensitive, 25
  See also separate listings
Sleep, 136, 161

Soap, 26, 31
  anti-bacterial, anti-acne, 31, 36, 45
  fatty acid based (superfatted), 32, 40, 45, 102, 120
  perfumed, 10, 12, 31, 36, 84, 88, 93, 99, 106, 134
Stress, effects of on skin, 116, 142, 150–52
"Studio One" (TV series), 177
Sudoriferous (sweat) glands, 12
Sun, exposure to, 116, 142
Sunburn, 20
Sun lamp, 147
Sun lotion, 144, 146
Sun sense, 143–47
  allergic skin, 143, 144
  minus skin, 143, 144–46
  plus skin, 143, 146–47
  sensitive skin, 143, 144
Superfatted cream, 32, 36, 40, 85, 94, 100, 103, 107, 120, 121
Superfatted soap, 32, 40, 45, 102, 120

Tanned complexion, face powder color for, 61
Tanning, daywear preparation for, 144, 145
Tea bag treatment

puffiness under eyes, 162
sensitive and allergic
    skins, 103–4
Teenage boys, shaving,
    87–88
Teenage girls, skin
    problems, 82–83, 87.
    See also Young
    complexion
1012 Soap, 31, 36, 84, 88,
    93, 99, 106
Tooth structure, 116
Translucent, face powder,
    61
Translucent Cameo, face
    powder, 61
Translucent Mist, face
    powder, 61
Translucent Suntan, face
    powder, 61
True skin, 12

Tweezing, eyebrow, 130
T-zone, 22–24, 29, 99

"U. S. Steel Hour" (TV
    series), 177

Valentino, 176
Vanderbilt, Gloria, 167–68
Vitamins, 140
Von Furstenburg, Ira, 176
Vreeland, Diana, 169

Waxing, unwanted facial
    hair, 129, 132
Westward Passage
    (movie), 177
White astringent, 32, 36,
    37, 41, 45, 80, 84, 85,
    86, 87, 88, 94, 97,
    100, 101, 103, 104,
    107, 130, 134, 150,

163, 167, 170, 173
White astringent compress,
    89–92
Whiteheads, 159–60
Wind, protection against,
    149–50
Windsor, Duchess of, 136,
    171–72
Winter care
    minus skin, 149–50
    plus skin, 150
Wool-induced rash, 163
Wrinkles/wrinkling, 15,
    19, 117
    under eyes, 161

Young complexion
    minus skin dryness
        problem, 110–12
    plus skin oiliness
        problem, 108–10